Essays 1958-1962
on
Atomic Physics
and Human Knowledge

1963
INTERSCIENCE PUBLISHERS
a division of JOHN WILEY & SONS
New York · London

Niels Bohr

Essays 1958-1962

on

Atomic Physics
and Human Knowledge

Printed in Great Britain by Richard Clay and Company, Ltd.,
Bungay, Suffolk

Preface

The present volume, which forms a sequel to two earlier collections of essays,[1] contains a number of articles written by Niels Bohr during the last five years of his life. The plans for the appearance of the present collection were made by my father some time ago, and the publication was awaiting only the final completion of the article *Light and Life Revisited*. The volume is now being published with the inclusion of the unfinished manuscript of this article.

The main theme of the first four essays may be said to be an elaboration and further development of the general viewpoints described in the earlier collections. It may therefore be appropriate to quote the following passage from the author's own introduction to the previous volume:

The importance of physical science for the development of general philosophical thinking rests not only on its contributions to our steadily increasing knowledge of that nature of which we ourselves are part, but also on the opportunities which time and again it has offered for examination and refinement of our conceptual tools. In our century, the study of the atomic constitution of matter has revealed an unsuspected limitation of the scope of

[1] N. Bohr, *Atomic Theory and the Description of Nature*, Cambridge University Press, 1934.
N. Bohr, *Atomic Physics and Human Knowledge*, John Wiley & Sons, New York, 1958.

classical physical ideas and has thrown new light on the demands on scientific explanation incorporated in traditional philosophy. The revision of the foundation for the unambiguous application of our elementary concepts, necessary for comprehension of atomic phenomena, therefore has a bearing far beyond the special domain of physical science.

The first essay describes the observational situation in quantum physics and the notion of complementarity. My father felt that, in this little article, he had succeeded in formulating some of the essential points more clearly and concisely than on earlier occasions.

In the second article, the complementary approach to problems of psychology and sociology is dealt with in more detail. A passage from a Danish novel, which my father had been very fond of from his youth, is used to illustrate a psychological situation in which complementary relationships are conspicuous.

The two following papers enter on the relationship between physics and biology, which through the years has deeply interested my father, and which he first discussed in the address *Light and Life* from 1932, included in the previous volume. He felt that some of his remarks from that time had not always been properly interpreted, and he was anxious to give an account of his views as they had developed since then, in particular under the stimulation of the great new discoveries in the field of molecular biology, which he had followed with such enthusiasm.

The subject is touched upon in the third article, written in 1960, but my father was hoping to take up the question in a more detailed paper based on a lecture he delivered in Cologne in June, 1962, with the title *Light and Life Revisited*. However, shortly afterwards, he became ill, and although he was well on his way to recovery and had resumed work on the article, it was not completed when he died, suddenly, on November 18th, 1962.

He left a manuscript which he had prepared as a basis for the lecture in Cologne and in which his views on the relationship between physics and biology are expounded in somewhat greater detail than in his earlier articles. It is, however, only with considerable hesitation that this manuscript is being published. Those familiar with my father's way of working will know what great efforts he devoted to the preparation of all his publications. The text would always be re-written many times while the matter was being gradually elucidated, and until a proper balance was achieved in the presentation of its various aspects. Although a great deal of work had been done on the present manuscript, it was still far from completion. It has nevertheless been included in the present volume, because of the interest which attaches to the views it contains, but the reader must bear in mind the preliminary character of their formulation. With regard to a few passages containing comments on specific biological problems, the author had planned major revisions. These passages have therefore been omitted from the text; their substance is indicated in notes inserted in small print.

The last three articles in the volume describe various phases in the development of atomic physics and quantum theory in the context of personal reminiscences. Frequently, in the company of colleagues, both older and younger, my father would enjoy recalling his vivid memories of the often dramatic events associated with the origin and gradual clarification of the new ideas. The preparation of these articles, written for various special occasions, led him to extensive historical studies, by which he would supplement his own memory by his rich personal correspondence from the periods in question, as well as by the published sources. The work on the Rutherford article extended over several years, during which he conferred with a large number of colleagues who had participated in the developments concerned. Although these three last papers are historical in character, they at the same time gave my father the opportunity to elucidate from new angles the general views which form the basic theme of the present as well as of the previous collections of essays.

In the preparation of the articles, my father was aided by Jørgen Kalckar, Aage Petersen and Erik Rüdinger. He would also have wished to express his appreciation of the effective help of Mrs S. Hellmann.

AAGE BOHR

Copenhagen
May 1963

Contents

Quantum Physics and Philosophy

Causality and Complementarity

1958

The significance of physical science for philosophy does not merely lie in the steady increase of our experience of inanimate matter, but above all in the opportunity of testing the foundation and scope of some of our most elementary concepts. Notwithstanding refinements of terminology due to accumulation of experimental evidence and developments of theoretical conceptions, all account of physical experience is, of course, ultimately based on common language, adapted to orientation in our surroundings and to tracing relationships between cause and effect. Indeed, Galileo's programme—to base the description of physical phenomena on measurable quantities—has afforded a solid foundation for the ordering of an ever larger field of experience.

In Newtonian mechanics, where the state of a system of material bodies is defined by their instantaneous positions and velocities, it proved possible, by the well-known simple principles, to derive, solely from the knowledge of the state of the system at a given time and of the forces acting upon the bodies, the state of the system at any other time. A description of this kind, which evidently represents an ideal form of causal relationships, expressed by the notion of *determinism*, was found to have still wider scope. Thus, in the account of electromagnetic phenomena, in which we have to consider a propagation of forces with finite velocities, a deterministic description could be upheld by including in the definition of the state not only the positions and velocities of the charged bodies, but also the direction and intensity of the electric and magnetic forces at every point of space at a given time. The situation in such respects was not essentially changed by the recognition, embodied in the notion of *relativity*, of the extent to which the description of physical phenomena depends on the reference frame chosen by the observer. We are here concerned with a most fruitful development which has made it possible to formulate physical laws common to all observers and to link phenomena which hitherto appeared uncorrelated. Although in this formulation use is made of mathematical abstractions such as a four-dimensional non-Euclidean metric, the physical interpretation for each observer rests on the usual separation between space and time, and maintains the deterministic character of the description. Since, moreover, as stressed by Einstein, the space–time coordination of different observers never implies reversal of what may be termed the causal sequence of events, relativity theory has not only widened the scope but also strengthened the foundation of the deterministic account, characteristic of the imposing edifice generally referred to as classical physics.

A new epoch in physical science was inaugurated, however, by Planck's discovery of the *elementary quantum of action*, which revealed a feature of *wholeness* inherent in atomic processes, going far beyond the ancient idea of the limited divisibility of matter. Indeed, it became clear that the pictorial description of classical physical theories represents an idealization valid only for phenomena in the analysis of which all actions involved are sufficiently large to permit the neglect of the quantum. While this condition is amply fulfilled in phenomena on the ordinary scale, we meet in experimental evidence concerning atomic particles with regularities of a novel type, incompatible with deterministic analysis. These quantal laws determine the peculiar stability and reactions of atomic systems, and are thus ultimately responsible for the properties of matter on which our means of observation depend.

The problem with which physicists were confronted was therefore to develop a rational generalization of classical physics, which would permit the harmonious incorporation of the quantum of action. After a preliminary exploration of the experimental evidence by more primitive methods, this difficult task was eventually accomplished by the introduction of appropriate mathematical abstractions. Thus, in the quantal formalism, the quantities by which the state of a physical system is ordinarily defined are replaced by symbolic operators subjected to a non-commutative algorism involving Planck's constant. This procedure prevents a fixation of such quantities to the extent which would be required for the deterministic description of classical physics, but allows us to determine their spectral distribution as revealed by evidence about atomic processes. In conformity with the non-pictorial character of the formalism, its physical interpretation finds expression in laws, of an essentially statistical type, pertaining to observations obtained under given experimental conditions.

Notwithstanding the power of quantum mechanics as a means of ordering an immense amount of evidence regarding atomic phenomena, its departure from accustomed demands of causal explanation has naturally given rise to the question whether we are here concerned with an exhaustive description of experience. The answer to this question evidently calls for a closer examination of the conditions for the unambiguous use of the concepts of classical physics in the analysis of atomic phenomena. The decisive point is to recognize that the description of the experimental arrangement and the recording of observations must be given in plain language, suitably refined by the usual physical terminology. This is a simple logical demand, since by the word "experiment" we can only mean a procedure regarding which we are able to communicate to others what we have done and what we have learnt.

In actual experimental arrangements, the fulfilment of such requirements is secured by the use, as measuring instruments, of rigid bodies sufficiently heavy to allow a completely classical account of their relative positions and velocities. In this connection, it is also essential to remember that all unambiguous information concerning atomic objects is derived from the permanent marks—such as a spot on a photographic plate, caused by the impact of an electron—left on the bodies which define the experimental conditions. Far from involving any special intricacy, the irreversible amplification effects on which the recording of the presence of atomic objects rests rather remind us of the essential irreversibility inherent in the very concept of observation. The description of atomic phenomena has in these respects a perfectly objective character, in the sense that no explicit reference is made to any individual observer and that therefore, with proper regard to relativistic exigencies, no ambiguity is involved in the communication of information.

As regards all such points, the observation problem of quantum physics in no way differs from the classical physical approach. The essentially new feature in the analysis of quantum phenomena is, however, the introduction of a *fundamental distinction between the measuring apparatus and the objects under investigation*. This is a direct consequence of the necessity of accounting for the functions of the

measuring instruments in purely classical terms, excluding in principle
any regard to the quantum of action. On their side, the quantal
features of the phenomenon are revealed in the information about the
atomic objects derived from the observations. While, within the scope
of classical physics, the interaction between object and apparatus can
be neglected or, if necessary, compensated for, in quantum physics
this interaction thus forms an inseparable part of the phenomenon.
Accordingly, the unambiguous account of proper quantum phenomena
must, in principle, include a description of all relevant features of the
experimental arrangement.

The very fact that repetition of the same experiment, defined on the
lines described, in general yields different recordings pertaining to the
object, immediately implies that a comprehensive account of experience in this field must be expressed by statistical laws. It need hardly
be stressed that we are not concerned here with an analogy to the
familiar recourse to statistics in the description of physical systems of
too complicated a structure to make practicable the complete definition
of their state necessary for a deterministic account. In the case of
quantum phenomena, the unlimited divisibility of events implied in
such an account is, in principle, excluded by the requirement to specify
the experimental conditions. Indeed, the feature of wholeness typical
of proper quantum phenomena finds its logical expression in the circumstance that any attempt at a well-defined subdivision would
demand a change in the experimental arrangement incompatible with
the definition of the phenomena under investigation.

Within the scope of classical physics, all characteristic properties of
a given object can in principle be ascertained by a single experimental
arrangement, although in practice various arrangements are often convenient for the study of different aspects of the phenomena. In fact,
data obtained in such a way simply supplement each other and can be
combined into a consistent picture of the behaviour of the object under
investigation. In quantum physics, however, evidence about atomic
objects obtained by different experimental arrangements exhibits a
novel kind of complementary relationship. Indeed, it must be recognized that such evidence which appears contradictory when combination into a single picture is attempted, exhausts all conceivable knowledge about the object. Far from restricting our efforts to put questions
to nature in the form of experiments, the notion of *complementarity*
simply characterizes the answers we can receive by such inquiry,
whenever the interaction between the measuring instruments and the
objects forms an integral part of the phenomena.

Although, of course, the classical description of the experimental arrangement and the irreversibility of the recordings concerning the atomic objects ensure a sequence of cause and effect conforming with elementary demands of causality, the irrevocable abandonment of the ideal of determinism finds striking expression in the complementary relationship governing the unambiguous use of the fundamental concepts on whose unrestricted combination the classical physical description rests. Indeed, the ascertaining of the presence of an atomic particle in a limited space–time domain demands an experimental arrangement involving a transfer of momentum and energy to bodies such as fixed scales and synchronized clocks, which cannot be included in the description of their functioning, if these bodies are to fulfil the role of defining the reference frame. Conversely, any strict application of the laws of conservation of momentum and energy to atomic processes implies, in principle, a renunciation of detailed space–time coordination of the particles.

These circumstances find quantitative expression in Heisenberg's indeterminacy relations which specify the reciprocal latitude for the fixation, in quantum mechanics, of kinematical and dynamical variables required for the definition of the state of a system in classical mechanics. In fact, the limited commutability of the symbols by which such variables are represented in the quantal formalism corresponds to the mutual exclusion of the experimental arrangements required for their unambiguous definition. In this context, we are of course not concerned with a restriction as to the accuracy of measurements, but with a limitation of the well-defined application of space–time concepts and dynamical conservation laws, entailed by the necessary distinction between measuring instruments and atomic objects.

In the treatment of atomic problems, actual calculations are most conveniently carried out with the help of a Schrödinger state function, from which the statistical laws governing observations obtainable under specified conditions can be deduced by definite mathematical operations. It must be recognized, however, that we are here dealing with a purely symbolic procedure, the unambiguous physical interpretation of which in the last resort requires a reference to a complete experimental arrangement. Disregard of this point has sometimes led to confusion, and in particular the use of phrases like "disturbance of phenomena by observation" or "creation of physical attributes of objects by measurements" is hardly compatible with common language and practical definition.

In this connection, the question has even been raised whether recourse to multivalued logics is needed for a more appropriate representation of the situation. From the preceding argumentation it will appear, however, that all departures from common language and ordinary logic are entirely avoided by reserving the word "phenomenon" solely for reference to unambiguously communicable information, in the account of which the word "measurement" is used in its plain meaning of standardized comparison. Such caution in the choice of terminology is especially important in the exploration of a new field of experience, where information cannot be comprehended in the familiar frame which in classical physics found such unrestricted applicability.

It is against this background that quantum mechanics may be seen to fulfil all demands on rational explanation with respect to consistency and completeness. Thus, the emphasis on permanent recordings under well-defined experimental conditions as the basis for a consistent interpretation of the quantal formalism corresponds to the presupposition, implicit in the classical physical account, that every step of the causal sequence of events in principle allows of verification. Moreover, a completeness of description like that aimed at in classical physics is provided by the possibility of taking every conceivable experimental arrangement into account.

Such argumentation does of course not imply that, in atomic physics, we have no more to learn as regards experimental evidence and the mathematical tools appropriate to its comprehension. In fact, it seems likely that the introduction of still further abstractions into the formalism will be required to account for the novel features revealed by the exploration of atomic processes of very high energy. The decisive point, however, is that in this connection there is no question of reverting to a mode of description which fulfils to a higher degree the accustomed demands regarding pictorial representation of the relationship between cause and effect.

The very fact that quantum regularities exclude analysis on classical lines necessitates, as we have seen, in the account of experience a logical distinction between measuring instruments and atomic objects, which in principle prevents comprehensive deterministic description. Summarizing, it may be stressed that, far from involving any arbitrary renunciation of the ideal of causality, the wider frame of complementarity directly expresses our position as regards the account of fundamental properties of matter presupposed in classical physical description, but outside its scope.

Notwithstanding all difference in the typical situations to which the notions of relativity and complementarity apply, they present in epistemological respects far-reaching similarities. Indeed, in both cases we are concerned with the exploration of harmonies which cannot be comprehended in the pictorial conceptions adapted to the account of more limited fields of physical experience. Still, the decisive point is that in neither case does the appropriate widening of our conceptual framework imply any appeal to the observing subject, which would hinder unambiguous communication of experience. In relativistic argumentation, such objectivity is secured by due regard to the dependence of the phenomena on the reference frame of the observer, while in complementary description all subjectivity is avoided by proper attention to the circumstances required for the well-defined use of elementary physical concepts.

In general philosophical perspective, it is significant that, as regards analysis and synthesis in other fields of knowledge, we are confronted with situations reminding us of the situation in quantum physics. Thus, the integrity of living organisms and the characteristics of conscious individuals and human cultures present features of wholeness, the account of which implies a typical complementary mode of description.[1] Owing to the diversified use of the rich vocabulary available for communication of experience in those wider fields, and above all to the varying interpretations, in philosophical literature, of the concept of causality, the aim of such comparisons has sometimes been misunderstood. However, the gradual development of an appropriate terminology for the description of the simpler situation in physical science indicates that we are not dealing with more or less vague analogies, but with clear examples of logical relations which, in different contexts, are met with in wider fields.

[1] Cf. N. Bohr, *Atomic Physics and Human Knowledge*, John Wiley & Sons, New York, 1958.

B

The Unity of Human Knowledge

1960

The question alluded to in the title for this address is as old as civilization itself, but has acquired renewed attention in our days with the increasing specialization of studies and social activities. From various sides concern has been expressed with the widespread confusion arising from the apparently divergent approaches taken by humanists and scientists to human problems, and in this connection there has even been talk about a cultural rift in modern society. We must, however, not forget that we are living in times of rapid developments in many fields of knowledge, reminiscent in such respect of the age of European Renaissance.

However great the difficulties of liberation from the medieval world view were felt at that time, the fruits of the so-called Scientific Revolution are certainly now a part of the common cultural background. In our century the immense progress of the sciences has not only greatly advanced technology and medicine, but has at the same time given us an unsuspected lesson about our position as observers of that nature of which we are part ourselves. Far from implying a schism between humanism and physical science, this development entails a message of importance for our attitude to common human problems, which—as I shall try to show—has given the old question of the unity of knowledge new perspective.

The pursuit of scientific inquiry with the aim of augmenting and

8

ordering our experience of the world around us has through the ages proved fertile, not least for the continual progress of technology which to so great an extent has changed the frame of our daily life. While early developments of astronomy, geodesy and metallurgy in Egypt, Mesopotamia, India and China were primarily directed to serve requirements of the community, it is in ancient Greece that we first meet with systematic endeavours to clarify the basic principles for the description and ordering of knowledge.

In particular, we admire the Greek mathematicians, who in many respects laid the firm foundation on which later generations have built. For our theme it is important to realize that the definition of mathematical symbols and operations is based on simple logical use of common language. Mathematics is therefore not to be regarded as a special branch of knowledge based on the accumulation of experience, but rather as a refinement of general language, supplementing it with appropriate tools to represent relations for which ordinary verbal expression is imprecise or too cumbersome.

In view of the apparent remoteness of mathematical abstractions, often frightening wider circles, it may be noted that even elementary mathematical training allows school disciples to see through the famous paradox of the race between Achilles and the tortoise. How could the fleet-footed hero ever catch up with and pass the slow reptile if it were given even the smallest handicap? Indeed, at his arrival at the starting point of the turtle, Achilles would find that it had moved to some further point along the race track, and this situation would be repeated in an infinite sequence. I need hardly remind you that the logical analysis of situations of this type was to play an important role in the development of mathematical concepts and methods.

From the beginning, the use of mathematics has been essential for the progress of the physical sciences. While Euclidean geometry sufficed for Archimedes' elucidation of fundamental problems of static equilibrium, the detailed description of the motion of material bodies demanded the development of the infinitesimal calculus on which the imposing edifice of Newtonian mechanics rests. Above all, the explanation of the orbital motion of the planets in our solar system, based on simple mechanical principles and the law of universal gravitation, deeply influenced the general philosophical attitude in the following centuries and strengthened the view that space and time as well as cause and effect had to be taken as *a priori* categories for the comprehension of all knowledge.

The extension of physical experience in our days has, however, necessitated a radical revision of the foundation for the unambiguous use of our most elementary concepts, and has changed our attitude to the aim of physical science. Indeed, from our present standpoint, physics is to be regarded not so much as the study of something *a priori* given, but rather as the development of methods for ordering and surveying human experience. In this respect our task must be to account for such experience in a manner independent of individual subjective judgment and therefore objective in the sense that it can be unambiguously communicated in the common human language.

As regards the very concepts of space and time reflected in the primitive use of words as here and there, and before and after, it is to be remembered how essential the immense speed of light propagation, compared with the velocities of the bodies in our neighbourhood, is for our ordinary orientation. However, the surprise that it proved impossible even by the most refined measurements to ascertain, in laboratory experiments, any effect of the orbital motion of the earth around the sun, revealed that the shape of rigid bodies and their mutual distances would be differently perceived by observers swiftly moving relative to each other, and that even events, which by one observer would be judged as simultaneous, by another could be reckoned as occurring at different moments. Far from giving rise to confusing complications, the recognition of the extent to which the account of physical experience depends on the standpoint of the observer proved most fertile in tracing fundamental laws valid for all observers.

Indeed, the general theory of relativity, by which Einstein in renouncing all ideas of absolute space and time gave our world picture a unity and harmony surpassing any previous dreams, offered an instructive lesson as regards the consistency and scope of plain language. Although the convenient formulation of the theory involves mathematical abstractions as four-dimensional non-Euclidean geometry, its physical interpretation rests fundamentally on every observer's possibility of maintaining a sharp separation between space and time and of surveying how any other observer, in his frame, will describe and coordinate experience by means of the common language.

New fundamental aspects of the observational problem, entailing a revision of the very foundation for the analysis of phenomena in terms of cause and effect, were to be uncovered by the development initiated by Planck's discovery of the universal quantum of action in the first year of this century. In fact, this discovery proved that the wide applicability of so-called classical physics rests entirely on the circumstance that the action involved in any phenomena on the ordinary scale is so large that the quantum can be completely neglected. In atomic processes, however, we meet with regularities of a novel kind, defying causal pictorial description but nevertheless responsible for the peculiar stability of atomic systems on which all properties of matter ultimately depend.

In this new field of experience, opened by modern refinements of the art of physical experimentation, we have met with many great surprises and even been faced with the problem of what kind of answers we can receive by putting questions to nature in the form of experiments. Indeed, in the account of ordinary experience it is taken for granted that the objects under investigation are not interfered with by the observation. It is true that when we look at the moon through a telescope we receive light from the sun reflected from the moon-surface, but the recoil from this reflection is far too small to have any effect on the position and velocity of a body as heavy as the moon. If, however, we have to do with atomic systems, whose constitution and reactions to external influence are fundamentally determined by the quantum of action, we are in a quite different position.

Faced with the question of how under such circumstances we can achieve an objective description, it is decisive to realize that however far the phenomena transcend the range of ordinary experience, the description of the experimental arrangement and the recording of observations must be based on common language. In actual experimentation this demand is amply satisfied with the specification of the experimental conditions through the use of heavy bodies such as diaphragms and photographic plates, the manipulation of which is accounted for in terms of classical physics. Just this circumstance, however, excludes any separate account of the interaction between the measuring instruments and the atomic objects under investigation.

Especially this situation prevents the unlimited combination of space–time coordination and the conservation laws of momentum and energy on which the causal pictorial description of classical physics rests. Thus, an experimental arrangement aiming at ascertaining where an atomic particle, whose position at a given time has been controlled, will be located at a later moment implies a transfer, uncontrollable in principle, of momentum and energy to the fixed scales and regulated clocks necessary for the definition of the reference frame. Conversely, the use of any arrangement suited to study momentum and energy balance—decisive for the account of essential properties of atomic systems—implies a renunciation of detailed space–time coordination of their constituent particles.

Under these circumstances it is not surprising that with one and the same experimental arrangement we may obtain different recordings corresponding to various individual quantum processes for the occurrence of which only statistical account can be given. Likewise we must be prepared that evidence, obtained by different, mutually exclusive experimental arrangements, may exhibit unprecedented contrast and even at first sight appear contradictory.

It is in this situation that the notion of complementarity is called for to provide a frame wide enough to embrace the account of fundamental regularities of nature which cannot be comprehended within a single picture. Indeed, evidence obtained under well-defined experimental conditions—and expressed by adequate use of elementary physical concepts—exhausts in its entirety all information about the atomic objects which can be communicated in common language.

A detailed account on complementary lines of a new wide domain of experience has been possible by the gradual establishment of a mathematical formalism, known as quantum mechanics, in which the elementary physical quantities are replaced by symbolic operators subject to an algorism, involving the quantum of action and reflecting the non-commutativity of the corresponding measuring operations. Just by treating the quantum of action as an element evading customary explanation—similar to the role of the velocity of light in relativity theory as a maximal speed of signals—this formalism can be regarded as a rational generalization of the conceptual framework of classical physics. For our theme, however, the decisive point is that the physical content of quantum mechanics is exhausted by its power to formulate statistical laws governing observations obtained under conditions specified in plain language.

The fact that in atomic physics, where we are concerned with regularities of unsurpassed exactness, objective description can be achieved only by including in the account of the phenomena explicit reference to the experimental conditions, emphasizes in a novel manner the inseparability of knowledge and our possibilities of inquiry. We are here concerned with a general epistemological lesson illuminating our position in many other fields of human interest.

In particular, the conditions of analysis and synthesis of so-called psychic experiences have always been an important problem in philosophy. It is evident that words like thoughts and sentiments, referring to mutually exclusive experiences, have been used in a typical complementary manner since the very origin of language. In this context, however, the subject–object separation demands special attention. Every unambiguous communication about the state and activity of our mind implies, of course, a separation between the content of our consciousness and the background loosely referred to as "ourselves", but any attempt at exhaustive description of the richness of conscious life demands in various situations a different placing of the section between subject and object.

In order to illustrate this important point, I shall allow myself to quote a Danish poet and philosopher, Poul Martin Møller, who lived about a hundred years ago and left behind an unfinished novel still read with delight by the older as well as the younger generation in this country. In his novel, called *The Adventures of a Danish Student*, the author gives a remarkably vivid and suggestive account of the interplay between the various aspects of our position, illuminated by discussions within a circle of students with different characters and divergent attitudes to life.

Especially I shall refer to a conversation between two cousins, one of whom is very soberly efficient in practical affairs, of the type which then, and even now, is known among students as a philistine, whereas the other, called the licentiate, is addicted to remote philosophical meditations detrimental to his social activities. When the philistine reproaches the licentiate for not having made up his mind to use the opportunities for finding a practical job, offered him by the kindness of his friends, the poor licentiate apologizes most sincerely, but explains the difficulties into which his reflections have brought him. Thus he says:

My endless enquiries make it impossible for me to achieve anything. Furthermore, I get to think about my own thoughts of the situation in which I find myself. I even think that I think of it, and divide myself into an infinite retrogressive sequence of "I"s who consider each other. I do not know at which "I" to stop as the actual, and in the moment I stop at one, there is indeed again an "I" which stops at it. I become confused and feel a dizziness as if I were looking down into a bottomless abyss, and my ponderings result finally in a terrible headache.

In his reply the cousin says:

I cannot in any way help you in sorting your many "I"s. It is quite outside my sphere of action, and I should either be or become as mad as you if I let myself in for your superhuman reveries. My line is to stick to palpable things and walk along the broad highway of common sense; therefore my "I"s never get tangled up.

Quite apart from the fine humour with which the story is told, it is certainly not easy to give a more pertinent account of essential aspects of the situation with which we all are faced. Fortunately, the risk of falling into the deplorable situation of the licentiate is small in normal life, where we become gradually accustomed to coping with practical necessities and learn to communicate in common language what we need and what is on our mind. In such adjustment the balance between seriousness and humour, conspicuous in children's play and equally appreciated in mature life, plays no small part.

The complementary way in which words like contemplation and volition are used has especially to be taken into account when turning to the problem of the freedom of will, discussed by philosophers through the ages. Even if we cannot say whether we want to do something because we gather that we can, or we can only do it because we will, the feeling of, so to speak, being able to make the best out of circumstances is a common human experience. Indeed, the notion of volition plays an indispensable part in human communication similar to words like hope and responsibility, in themselves equally undefinable outside the context in which they are used.

The flexibility of the subject–object separation in the account of conscious life corresponds to a richness of experience so multifarious that it involves a variety of approaches. As regards our knowledge of fellow beings, we witness, of course, only their behaviour, but we must realize that the word consciousness is unavoidable when such behaviour is so complex that its account in common language entails reference to self-awareness. It is evident, however, that all search for an ultimate subject is at variance with the aim of objective description, which demands the contraposition of subject and object.

Such considerations involve no lack of appreciation of the inspiration which the great creations of art offer us by pointing to features of harmonious wholeness in our position. Indeed, in renouncing logical analysis to an increasing degree and in turn allowing the play on all strings of emotion, poetry, painting and music contain possibilities of bridging between extreme modes as those characterized as pragmatic and mystic. Conversely, already ancient Indian thinkers understood the logical difficulties in giving exhaustive expression for such wholeness. In particular, they found escape from apparent disharmonies in life by stressing the futility of demanding an answer to the question of the meaning of existence, realizing that any use of the word "meaning" implies comparison; and with what can we compare the whole existence?

The aim of our argumentation is to emphasize that all experience, whether in science, philosophy or art, which may be helpful to mankind, must be capable of being communicated by human means of expression, and it is on this basis that we shall approach the question of unity of knowledge. Confronted with the great diversity of cultural developments, we may therefore search for those features in all civilizations which have their roots in the common human situation. Especially we recognize that the position of the individual within the community exhibits in itself multifarious, often mutually exclusive, aspects.

When approaching the age-old problem of the foundation of so-called ethical values we shall in the first place ask about the scope of such concepts as justice and charity, the closest possible combination of which is attempted in all human societies. Still it is evident that a situation permitting unambiguous use of accepted judicial rules leaves no room for the free display of charity. But, as stressed especially by the famous Greek tragedians, it is equally clear that compassion can bring everyone in conflict with any concisely formulated idea of justice. We are here confronted with complementary relationships inherent in the human position, and unforgettably expressed in old Chinese philosophy, reminding us that in the great drama of existence we are ourselves both actors and spectators.

In comparing different national cultures we meet with the special difficulty of appreciating the culture of one nation in terms of the traditions of another. In fact, the element of complacency inherent in every culture corresponds closely to the instinct of self-preservation characteristic of any species among the living organisms. In such context it is, however, important to realize that the mutually exclusive characteristics of cultures, resting on traditions fostered by historical events, cannot be immediately compared to those met with in physics, psychology and ethics, where we are dealing with intrinsic features of the common human situation.

In fact, as is not least conspicuous in European history, contact between nations has often resulted in the fusion of cultures retaining valuable elements of the original national traditions. The question of how to ameliorate the so-called cultural rift in modern societies, which has attracted so much attention at this meeting, is after all a more restricted educational problem, the attitude to which would seem to call not only for information but, as I think everyone will agree, also for some humour. A most serious task is, however, to promote mutual understanding between nations with very different cultural backgrounds.

Indeed, the rapid progress of science and technology in our days, which entails unique promises for the promotion of human welfare and at the same time imminent menaces to universal security, presents our whole civilization with a veritable challenge. Certainly, every increase in knowledge and potentialities has always implied a greater

responsibility, but at the present moment, when the fate of all peoples
is inseparably connected, a collaboration in mutual confidence, based
on appreciation of every aspect of the common human position, is
more necessary than ever before in the history of mankind.

The Connection between the Sciences

1960

It is with great pleasure, although not without hesitation, that I have accepted the kind invitation to speak at the opening of this International Congress of Pharmaceutic Sciences. As a physicist I have, of course, no such insight in the field of pharmacy as is possessed in richest measure by the many distinguished scientists from different countries who are here assembled. At this occasion, however, it may be appropriate to comment on the intimate connection between our knowledge in all branches of science. This connection was indeed emphasized with vigour and enthusiasm by Hans Christian Ørsted, who established the first regulated pharmaceutic examination in Denmark, and it was to him a constant source of inspiration in his fundamental scientific researches and his many-sided and fruitful activity in the Danish community.

Experience of the help which substances occurring in nature can afford for the cure of human disease goes back to the infancy of civilization, when the conception of rational scientific inquiry was still unknown. Yet, it is interesting to recall how much the search for medical herbs in woods and meadows has stimulated the development of systematic botany. Furthermore, the preparation of medicaments and the study of their effects were to prove of essential importance for the progress of chemistry.

For a long time the study of the properties and transformations of substances stood conspicuously apart from the endeavours, characteristic of the approach in physics, to account for the behaviour of the bodies in our surroundings in terms of space and time, and cause and effect. Indeed, this was the foundation for the whole edifice of Newtonian mechanics and even electromagnetic theory based on Ørsted's and Faraday's discoveries, which through their technological applications have so largely changed the frame of our daily life.

The development in the former century of the ancient ideas of the atomic constitution of matter stimulated the search for a closer connection between chemistry and physics. On the one hand, the clarification of the concept of chemical elements led to the understanding of the laws governing the proportions in which these elements enter into chemical combinations. On the other hand, the study of the remarkably simple properties of gases led to the development of the mechanical theory of heat, offering an explanation of the general laws of thermodynamics which have found such fruitful application, not least in physical chemistry.

Studies of thermal radiative equilibrium, based on electromagnetic theory, were, however, to disclose a feature of wholeness in atomic processes, irreconcilable with the ideas of classical physics. Indeed, Planck's discovery of the universal quantum of action taught us that the wide applicability of the accustomed description of the behaviour of matter in bulk rests entirely on the circumstance that the action involved in phenomena on the ordinary scale is so large that the quantum can be completely neglected. In individual atomic processes, however, we meet with regularities of a novel kind, responsible for the peculiar stability of atomic systems on which all properties of matter ultimately depend.

The ordering of this new rich field of experience has demanded a radical revision of the foundation for the unambiguous use of our most elementary physical concepts. To account for what we actually do and learn in physical experimentation, it is, of course, necessary to describe the experimental arrangement and the recording of observations in common language. In the study of atomic phenomena, however, we are presented with a situation where the repetition of an experiment with the same arrangement may lead to different recordings, and experiments with different arrangements may give results which at first sight seem contradictory to each other.

The elucidation of these apparent paradoxes has been brought about by the recognition that the interaction between the objects under investigation and our tools of observation, which in ordinary experience can be neglected or taken into account separately, forms, in the domain of quantum physics, an inseparable part of the phenomena. Indeed, under such conditions experience cannot be combined in the accustomed manner, but the phenomena must be considered as complementary to each other in the sense that they together exhaust all information about the atomic objects which can be unambiguously expressed.

The proper mathematical tools for a comprehensive description on complementary lines have been created by the so-called quantum mechanical formalism by which we have to such an extent been able to account for the physical and chemical properties of matter. The humorous dispute between physicists and chemists as to whether chemistry has been swallowed by physics or physics become chemistry illustrates the character and scope of this progress.

It will carry us much too far from our theme to mention in detail the great development of atomic science in our days, and I shall only briefly remind that, in the binding of the electrons to the nucleus of the atom and in the role they play for the joining of the atoms in molecules of chemical compounds, we have to do with typical quantum effects resisting accustomed pictorial representation. Due to the large mass of the nuclei compared with that of the electrons, it is, however, possible to account with high approximation for the atomic configuration in the molecules, corresponding to the well-known structural formulae which have proved so indispensable in the ordering of chemical evidence.

The whole approach is not only in complete accordance with the usual chemical kinetics, but even stresses the simple assumptions on which it is based. Thus, in any process resulting in chemical combinations, the properties of the new molecules do not primarily depend on the composition of the molecules by whose interaction they were formed, but only on the relative placing of the atoms of which they consist. Any secondary characteristics of the state of such molecules, corresponding to oscillations left from their formation, will indeed not essentially affect their chemical properties and will even, due to the general thermal agitations in the medium, rapidly lose all connection with their previous history.

The general understanding of the specific properties of matter, to which the quantum of action provided a clue, has initiated a period of rapid growth of the natural sciences, reminiscent in many respects of the scientific revolution in the sixteenth and seventeenth centuries. Among the most impressive of these developments is the modern rise of biochemistry which has been equally beneficial to physiology and pharmacology. In particular, the widegoing obliteration of the distinction between organic and inorganic chemistry has raised anew the old problem of the extent to which the physical sciences can account for the display of life.

The gradual recognition, through the development of anatomy and physiology, of the immense complexity of the structure of living organisms and the multifarious refined regulative mechanisms governing their function, has often led to doubts whether the maintenance of order in the organism is compatible with the general laws of thermodynamics. Still, from the standpoint of modern chemical kinetics, no such departure is to be expected, and thorough investigations into the exchange of energy and entropy accompanying the metabolism and movements of the organisms have in fact never disclosed any restriction of thermodynamical principles.

In the last years, great progress has been achieved as regards our knowledge of the complicated molecular structures in living cells, and especially of the specific molecular chains which carry the genetic information from generation to generation. Further, our insight into the enzymatic processes by which this information serves to direct the formation of other specific molecular structures, such as the proteins, is steadily increasing. In fact, for all we know, we may have here to do with a steady increase in the stability of the constitution of the cells with an expenditure of free energy corresponding to the increase of entropy in usual irreversible chemical processes.

On this background the view suggests itself that, in the whole life of the organism, we have to do with processes of not immediately reversible character, corresponding to an ever-increasing stability under the prevailing conditions maintained by nutrition and respiration. In spite of all differences of scale and function, we are here faced with a far-reaching similarity between living organisms and automatic machines. Indeed, on the basis of recent advances in technology, it is possible to design machines reacting in any prescribed manner, including their own repair and reproduction, provided that they have access to the necessary materials and energy sources.

Still, as regards the much-debated question concerning the comparison between organisms and machines, it is essential to keep in mind that organic life is a manifestation of nature's resources far beyond those used for the construction of machines. In fact, in the account of the functioning of devices for calculation and control we can essentially disregard the atomic constitution of matter and confine ourselves to the account of the mechanical and electrical properties of the materials used and to the application of the simple physical laws governing the interaction between the parts of the machine. However, the whole history of organic evolution presents us with the results of the trying out in nature of the immense possibilities of atomic inter-actions.

Because of their immense complexity, it is not surprising that the organisms reveal properties and potentialities which are in striking contrast with those exhibited by so-called inanimate matter under simple reproducible experimental conditions. It is on this background that such notions as purposefulness and self-preservation, referring to the behaviour of organisms as entities, have found fruitful application in biological research.

In the discussions of the foundations of biology the question of the role of notions beyond the language of physics has formed a main topic. From the one side the view has been expressed that such concepts, despite their evident fertility, would eventually prove superfluous. From the other side it has been argued that we have here to do with irreducible elements in any account of the display of life.

The lesson as regards our position as observers of nature which quantum physics has taught us has given a new background to such discussions. Indeed, this lesson suggests that the situation as regards objective description of biological phenomena reflects different approaches in ordinary physiology and modern biochemistry. The basis for the complementary mode of description in biology is not connected with the problems of controlling the interaction between object and measuring tool, already taken into account in chemical kinetics, but with the practically inexhaustible complexity of the organism.

This situation can hardly be regarded as being of temporary charac-ter, but would rather seem to be inherently connected with the way in which our whole conceptual framework has developed from serving the more primitive necessities of daily life to coping with the growth of knowledge gained by systematic scientific research. Thus, as long as the word "life" is retained for practical or epistemological reasons, the dual approach in biology will surely persist.

In our discussion we have so far considered living organisms as objects under investigation, in a way similar to that in which we strive to comprehend experience of any other part of nature. When we approach the problems of psychology we enter into a new domain of knowledge where the question of analysis and synthesis has attracted vivid interest through the ages. The language which we use in social intercourse to communicate our state of mind is indeed very different from that usually employed in the physical sciences. Thus, words like contemplation and volition, referring to situations which are mutually exclusive but equally characteristic of conscious life, have been used in a typical complementary manner since the very origin of language.

The close relationship between psychical experience and physical and chemical processes in our body is evidenced not least by the application of medicaments in mental disease. The irreversible character of the physiological processes concerned is also clearly reflected by the degree to which all that has ever come to consciousness can be remembered. It is, of course, tempting to pursue such considerations, but at each further step new difficulties turn up, inherently connected with the limited scope of the concepts available for such inquiry.

In this address I have tried to show how researches into the world of atoms have offered new opportunities of tracing that harmony in nature of which Ørsted spoke, but which we perhaps would rather refer to as the unity of human knowledge. It is indeed only the appreciation of such harmony or unity which can help us to keep a balanced attitude to our position and avoid that confusion which the tumultuous progress of science and technology in almost every field of human interest may so easily produce. The programme of this congress bears witness to the fact that the pharmaceutic and pharmacological sciences represent an integral part of that inquiry into the wonders of nature by which we strive to promote human understanding and welfare. With the hope that your meeting will contribute to this great goal, I want to express my warmest wishes that it will be an inspiring experience to you all.

Light and Life Revisited[1]

1962

It is a great pleasure for me to follow the invitation of my old friend Max Delbrück to speak at the inauguration of this new Institute of Genetics at the University of Cologne. Of course, as a physicist I have no first-hand knowledge of the extensive and rapidly developing field of research to which this Institute is devoted, but I welcome Delbrück's suggestion to comment upon some general considerations about the relationship between biology and atomic physics, which I presented in an address entitled *Light and Life*, delivered at an International Congress on Radiation Therapy in Copenhagen thirty years ago. Delbrück, who at that time was working with us in Copenhagen as a physicist, took great interest in such considerations which, as he has been kind enough to say, stimulated his interest in biology and presented him with a challenge in his successful researches in genetics.

The place of living organisms within general physical experience has through the ages attracted the attention of scientists and philosophers. Thus, the integrity of the organisms was felt by Aristotle to present a fundamental difficulty for the assumption of a limited divisibility of matter, in which the school of atomists sought a basis for the understanding of the order reigning in nature in spite of the variety of physical phenomena. Conversely, Lucretius, summing up the arguments for atomic theory, interpreted the growth of a plant from its seed

[1] Unfinished manuscript (see Preface).

as evidence for the permanence of some elementary structure during the development, a consideration strikingly reminiscent of the approach in modern genetics.

Still, after the development of classical mechanics in the Renaissance and its subsequent fruitful application to the atomistic interpretation of the laws of thermodynamics, the upholding of order in the complicated structure and functions of the organisms was often thought to present unsurmountable difficulties. A new background for the attitude towards such problems was, however, created by the discovery of the quantum of action in the first year of our century, which revealed a feature of individuality in atomic processes going far beyond the ancient doctrine of the limited divisibility of matter. Indeed, this discovery provided a clue to the remarkable stability of atomic and molecular systems on which the properties of the substances composing our tools as well as our bodies ultimately depend.

The considerations in my address referred to were inspired by the recent completion of a logically consistent formalism of quantum mechanics. This development has essentially clarified the conditions for an objective account in atomic physics, involving the elimination of all subjective judgment. The crucial point is that, even though we have to do with phenomena outside the grasp of a deterministic pictorial description, we must employ common language, suitably refined by the terminology of classical physics, to communicate what we have done and what we have learned by putting questions to nature in the form of experiments. In actual physical experimentation this requirement is fulfilled by using as measuring instruments rigid bodies such as diaphragms, lenses, and photographic plates sufficiently large and heavy to allow an account of their shape and relative positions and displacements without regard to any quantum features inherently involved in their atomic constitution.

In classical physics we assume that phenomena can be subdivided without limit, and that especially the interaction between the measuring instruments and the object under investigation can be disregarded or at any rate compensated for. However, the feature of individuality in atomic processes, represented by the universal quantum of action, implies that in quantum physics this interaction is an integral part of the phenomena, for which no separate account can be given if the instruments shall serve their purpose of defining the experimental arrangement and the recording of the observations. The circumstance that such recordings, like the spot produced on a photographic plate by the impact of an electron, involve essentially irreversible processes presents no special difficulty for the interpretation of the experiments, but rather stresses the irreversibility which is implied in principle in the very concept of observation.

The fact that in one and the same well-defined experimental arrangement we generally obtain recordings of different individual processes thus makes indispensable the recourse to a statistical account of quantum phenomena. Moreover, the impossibility of combining phenomena observed under different experimental arrangements into a single classical picture implies that such apparently contradictory phenomena must be regarded as complementary in the sense that, taken together, they exhaust all well-defined knowledge about the atomic objects. Indeed, any logical contradiction in these respects is excluded by the mathematical consistency of the formalism of quantum mechanics, which serves to express the statistical laws holding for observations made under any given set of experimental conditions.

For our theme it is of decisive importance that the fundamental feature of complementarity in quantum physics, adapted as it is to the clarification of the well-known paradoxes concerning the dual character of electromagnetic radiation and material particles, is equally conspicuous in the account of the properties of atomic and molecular systems. Thus, any attempt at space–time location of the electrons in atoms and molecules would demand an experimental arrangement prohibiting the appearance of spectral regularities and chemical bonds. Still, the fact that the atomic nuclei are very much heavier than the electrons allows the fixation of the relative positions of the atoms within molecular structures to an extent sufficient to give concrete significance to the structural formulae which have proved so fruitful in chemical research. Indeed, renouncing pictorial description of the electronic constitution of the atomic systems and only making use of empirical knowledge of threshold and binding energies in molecular processes, we can within a wide field of experience treat the reactions of such systems by ordinary chemical kinetics, based on the well-established laws of thermodynamics.

These remarks apply not least to biophysics and biochemistry, in which in our century we have witnessed such extraordinary progress. Of course, the practically uniform temperature within the organisms reduces the thermodynamical requirements to constancy or steady decrease of free energy. Thus, the assumption suggests itself that the formation of all permanently or temporarily present macromolecular structures represents essentially irreversible processes which increase the stability of the organism under the prevailing conditions kept up by nutrition and respiration. Also the photo-synthesis in plants is of course, as recently discussed by Britten and Gamow, accompanied by an overall increase in entropy.

Notwithstanding such general considerations, it appeared for a long time that the regulatory functions in living organisms, disclosed especially by studies of cell physiology and embryology, exhibited a fineness so unfamiliar to ordinary physical and chemical experience as to point to the existence of fundamental biological laws without counterpart in the properties of inanimate matter studied under simple reproducible experimental conditions. Stressing the difficulties of keeping the organisms alive under conditions which aim at a full atomic account I therefore suggested that the very existence of life might be taken as a basic fact in biology in the same sense as the quantum of action has to be regarded in atomic physics as a fundamental element irreducible to classical physical concepts.

In reconsidering this conjecture from our present standpoint, it must be kept in mind that the task of biology cannot be that of accounting for the fate of each of the innumerable atoms permanently or temporarily included in a living organism. In the study of regulatory biological mechanisms the situation is rather that no sharp distinction can be made between the detailed construction of these mechanisms and the functions they fulfil in upholding the life of the whole organism. Indeed, many terms used in practical physiology reflect a procedure of research in which, starting from the recognition of the functional role of the parts of the organism, one aims at a physical and chemical account of their finer structures and of the processes in which they are involved. Surely, as long as for practical or epistemological reasons one speaks of life, such teleological terms will be used in complementing the terminology of molecular biology. This circumstance, however, does not in itself imply any limitation in the application to biology of the well-established principles of atomic physics.[1]

To approach this fundamental question it is essential to distinguish between separate atomic processes taking place within small spatial extensions and completed within short time intervals, and the constitution and functions of larger structures formed by the agglomeration of molecules keeping together for periods comparable to or exceeding the cycle of cell division. Even such structural elements of the organism often display properties and a behaviour which imply an

[1] In the lecture in Cologne (which was given in German) the author inserted the following phrase: In the last resort, it is a matter of how one makes headway in biology. I think that the feeling of wonder which the physicists had thirty years ago has taken a new turn. Life will always be a wonder, but what changes is the balance between the feeling of wonder and the courage to try to understand. (Translated from the transcript of the tape recording.)

organization of a more specific kind than that exhibited by the parts of any machine we are able to construct. Indeed, the functions of the building blocks of modern mechanical and electromagnetic calculation devices are determined simply by their shape and by such ordinary material properties as mechanical rigidity, electric conductivity and magnetic susceptibility. As far as the construction of machines is concerned, such materials are formed once and for all by more or less regular crystalline accumulations of atoms, while in the living organisms we have to do with a remarkable rhythm of another kind where molecular polymerisation which, when carried on indefinitely, would make the organism as dead as a crystal, is time and again interrupted.

A paragraph is here omitted, commenting on the isotopic tracer investigations by Hevesy, which showed that a major part of the calcium atoms incorporated in the skeleton of a mouse at the fœtal stage remains there for the whole life of the animal. The author discussed the problem of how the organism is able to economize with its calcium to such a remarkable extent during the growth of the skeleton.

The application of physical methods and viewpoints has led to great progress in many other fields of biology. Impressive examples are the recent discoveries of the fine structure of muscles and of the transport of the materials used for the activity of the nerves. At the same time as these discoveries add to our knowledge of the complexity of the organisms, they point to possibilities of physical mechanisms which hitherto have escaped notice. In genetics, the early studies by Timofjeev-Ressofskij, Zimmer and Delbrück of the mutations produced by penetrating radiation permitted the first approximate evaluation of the spatial extensions within the chromosomes critical for the stability of the genes. A turning-point in this whole field came, however, about ten years ago with Crick and Watson's ingenious proposal for an interpretation of the structure of the DNA molecules. I vividly remember how Delbrück, in telling me about the discovery, said that it might lead to a revolution in microbiology comparable with the development of atomic physics, initiated by Rutherford's nuclear model of the atom.

In this connection I may also recall how Christian Anfinsen in his lecture at a symposium in Copenhagen a few years ago started by saying that he and his colleagues had hitherto considered themselves learned geneticists and biochemists, but that now they felt like amateurs trying to make head and tail of more or less separated biochemical evidence. The situation he pictured was, indeed, strikingly similar to that which confronted physicists by the discovery of the atomic nucleus, which to so unsuspected a degree completed our knowledge about the structure of the atom, challenging us to find out how it could be used for ordering the accumulated information about the physical and chemical properties of matter. As is well known, this goal was largely achieved within a few decades by the cooperation of a whole generation of physicists, which in intensity and scope resembles that taking place in these years in genetics and molecular biology.

A section is here omitted, commenting on the problem of the rhythm in the process of growth of a cell. The author in particular discussed the control of the DNA duplication and the role which the structure of the chromosomes may play in this process as well as in the stability of the genetic material. He further considered the possibility that the duplication process is intimately associated with the transfer of information from DNA.

Before I conclude, I should like briefly to call attention to the source of biological knowledge which the so-called psychical experience connected with life may offer. I need hardly stress that the word consciousness presents itself in the description of a behaviour so complicated that its communication implies reference to the individual organism's awareness of itself. Moreover, words like thoughts and sentiments refer to mutually exclusive experiences and have therefore since the origin of human language been used in a typically complementary manner. Of course, in objective physical description no reference is made to the observing subject, while in speaking of conscious experience we say "I think" or "I feel". The analogy to the demand of taking all essential features of the experimental arrangement into account in quantum physics is, however, reflected by the different verbs we attach to the pronoun.

The fact that every thing which has come into our consciousness is remembered points to its leaving permanent marks in the organism. Of course we are only here concerned with novel experiences of importance for action or contemplation. Thus, we are normally unconscious of our respiration and the beating of the heart, and hardly aware of the working of our muscles and bones during the motion of our limbs. However, by the reception of sense impressions on which we act at the moment or later, some irreversible modification occurs in the nervous system, resulting in a new adjustment. Without entering on any more or less naïve picture of the localization and integration of the activity of the brain it is tempting to compare such adjustment to irreversible processes by which stability in the novel situation is restored. Of course, only the possibility of such processes but not their actual traces are hereditary, leaving coming generations unencumbered by the

history of thinking, however valuable it may be for their educa-
tion.

In expressing the warmest wishes for the success of the investigations
of the distinguished group of scientists working in this new and
magnificently equipped Institute, I cannot think of a better prospect
than that it will contribute to increase our insight into that order of
nature which it was the original aim of the atomic conception to
account for.

Note: In the editing of the manuscript for publication, a few minor altera-
tions of formal character have been made.

The Rutherford Memorial Lecture
1958 [1]

Reminiscences of the Founder of Nuclear Science and of Some Developments Based on his Work

1961

It has been a pleasure for me to accept the invitation from The Physical Society to contribute to the series of Rutherford Memorial Lectures in which, through the years, several of Rutherford's closest collaborators have commented on his fundamental scientific achievements and communicated reminiscences about his great human personality. As one who in early youth had the good fortune to join the group of physicists working under Rutherford's inspiration, and owes so much to his warm friendship through the many succeeding years, I welcome the task of recalling some of my most treasured remembrances. Since it is impossible, of course, in a single lecture to attempt a survey of the immense and many-sided life-work of Ernest Rutherford and its far-reaching consequences, I shall confine myself to periods of which I have personal recollections and to developments I have followed at close hand.

I

The first time I had the great experience of seeing and listening to Rutherford was in the autumn of 1911 when, after my university studies in Copenhagen, I was working in Cambridge with J. J. Thomson, and

---

[1] The present text is an elaborated version, completed in 1961, of the lecture delivered without a prepared manuscript at a meeting of The Physical Society of London at the Imperial College of Science and Technology on November 28th, 1958.

Rutherford came down from Manchester to speak at the annual Cavendish Dinner. Although on this occasion I did not come into personal contact with Rutherford, I received a deep impression of the charm and power of his personality by which he had been able to achieve almost the incredible wherever he worked. The dinner took place in a most humorous atmosphere and gave the opportunity for several of Rutherford's colleagues to recall some of the many anecdotes which already then were attached to his name. Among various illustrations of how intensely he was absorbed in his researches, a laboratory assistant in the Cavendish was reported to have noted that, of all the eager young physicists who through the years had worked in the famous laboratory, Rutherford was the one who could swear at his apparatus most forcefully.

From Rutherford's own address I especially remember the warmth with which he greeted the latest success of his old friend C. T. R. Wilson, who by the ingenious cloud chamber method had just then obtained the first photographs of tracks of α-rays exhibiting clear cases of sharp bends in their usual remarkably straight path. Of course, Rutherford was thoroughly acquainted with the phenomenon which only a few months before had led him to his epoch-making discovery of the atomic nucleus, but that such details of the life history of α-rays could now be witnessed directly by our eyes, he admitted to be a surprise, causing him extreme pleasure. In this connection Rutherford spoke most admiringly of the persistence with which Wilson already during their comradeship in the Cavendish had pursued his researches on cloud formation with ever more refined apparatus. As Wilson later told me, his interest in these beautiful phenomena had been awakened when as a youth he was watching the appearance and disappearance of fogs as air currents ascended the Scottish mountain ridges and again descended in the valleys.

A few weeks after the Cavendish Dinner I went up to Manchester to visit one of my recently deceased father's colleagues who was also a close friend of Rutherford. There, I again had the opportunity to see Rutherford who in the meantime had attended the inaugural meeting of the Solvay Council in Brussels, where he had met Planck and Einstein for the first time. During the conversation, in which Rutherford spoke with characteristic enthusiasm about the many new prospects in physical science, he kindly assented to my wish to join the group working in his laboratory when, in the early spring of 1912, I should have finished my studies in Cambridge where I had been deeply interested in J. J. Thomson's original ideas on the electronic constitution of atoms.

In those days, many young physicists from various countries had gathered around Rutherford, attracted by his genius as a physicist and by his unique gifts as a leader of scientific cooperation. Although Rutherford was always intensely occupied with the progress of his own work, he had the patience to listen to every young man, when he felt he had any idea, however modest, on his mind. At the same time, with his whole independent attitude, he had only little respect for authority and could not stand what he called "pompous talk". On such occasions he could even sometimes speak in a boyish way about venerable colleagues, but he never permitted himself to enter into personal controversies, and he used to say: "There is only one person who can take away one's good name, and that is oneself!"

Naturally, to trace in every direction the consequences of the discovery of the atomic nucleus was the centre of interest of the whole Manchester group. In the first weeks of my stay in the laboratory, I followed, on Rutherford's advice, an introductory course on the experimental methods of radioactive research which under the experienced instruction of Geiger, Makower and Marsden was arranged for the benefit of students and new visitors. However, I rapidly became absorbed in the general theoretical implications of the new atomic model and especially in the possibility it offered of a sharp distinction as regards the physical and chemical properties of matter, between those directly originating in the atomic nucleus itself and those primarily depending on the distribution of the electrons bound to it at distances very large compared with nuclear dimensions.

While the explanation of the radioactive disintegrations had to be sought in the intrinsic constitution of the nucleus, it was evident that the ordinary physical and chemical characteristics of the elements manifested properties of the surrounding electron system. It was even clear that, owing to the large mass of the nucleus and its small extension compared with that of the whole atom, the constitution of the electron system would depend almost exclusively on the total electric charge of the nucleus. Such considerations at once suggested the prospect of basing the account of the physical and chemical properties of every element on a single integer, now generally known as the atomic number, expressing the nuclear charge as a multiple of the elementary unit of electricity.

In the development of such views, I was encouraged not least by discussions with George Hevesy who distinguished himself among the Manchester group by his uncommonly broad chemical knowledge. In particular, as early as 1911, he had conceived the ingenious tracer method which has since become so powerful a tool in chemical and biological research. As Hevesy has himself humorously described, he was led to this method by the negative results of elaborate work undertaken as a response to a challenge by Rutherford who had told him that, "if he was worth his salt", he ought to be helpful by separating the valuable radium D from the large amount of lead chloride extracted from pitchblende and presented to Rutherford by the Austrian Government.

My views took more definite shape in conversations with Hevesy about the wonderful adventure of those Montreal and Manchester years, in which Rutherford and his collaborators, after the discoveries of Becquerel and Madame Curie, had built up the science of radioactivity by progressively disentangling the succession and interconnections of radioactive disintegrations. Thus, when I learned that the number of stable and decaying elements already identified exceeded the available places in the famous table of Mendeleev, it struck me that such chemically inseparable substances, to the existence of which Soddy had early called attention and which later by him were termed "isotopes", possessed the same nuclear charge and differed only in the mass and intrinsic structure of the nucleus. The immediate conclusion was that by radioactive decay the element, quite independently of any change in its atomic weight, would shift its place in the periodic table by two steps down or one step up, corresponding to the decrease or increase in the nuclear charge accompanying the emission of α- or β-rays, respectively.

When I turned to Rutherford to learn his reaction to such ideas, he expressed, as always, alert interest in any promising simplicity but warned with characteristic caution against overstressing the bearing of the atomic model and extrapolating from comparatively meagre experimental evidence. Still, such views, probably originating from many sides, were at that time lively discussed within the Manchester group, and evidence in their support was rapidly forthcoming, especially through chemical investigations by Hevesy as well as by Russell.

In particular, a strong support for the idea of the atomic number as determining the general physical properties of the elements was obtained from spectroscopic investigations by Russell and Rossi of mixtures of ionium and thorium, which pointed to the identity of the optical spectra of these two substances in spite of their different radioactive properties and atomic weights. On the basis of an analysis of the whole evidence then available, the general relationship between the specified radioactive processes and the resulting change of the atomic number of the element was indicated by Russell in a lecture to the Chemical Society in the late autumn of 1912.

In this connection it is interesting that, when after further research, especially by Fleck, the radioactive displacement law in its complete form was enunciated a few months later by Soddy working in Glasgow, as well as by Fajans in Karlsruhe, these authors did not recognize its close relation to the fundamental features of Rutherford's atomic model, and Fajans even regarded the change in chemical properties evidently connected with the electron constitution of the atoms as a strong argument against a model according to which the α- as well as the β-rays had their origin in the nucleus. About the same time, the idea of the atomic number was independently introduced by van den Broek in Amsterdam, but in his classification of the elements a different nuclear charge was still ascribed to every stable or radioactive substance.

So far, the primary objects of the discussions within the Manchester group were the immediate consequences of the discovery of the atomic nucleus. The general programme of interpreting the accumulated experience about the ordinary physical and chemical properties of matter on the basis of the Rutherford model of the atom presented, however, more intricate problems, which were to be clarified gradually in the succeeding years. Thus, in 1912, there could only be question of a preliminary orientation as to the general features of the situation.

From the outset it was evident that, on the basis of the Rutherford model, the typical stability of atomic systems could by no means be reconciled with classical principles of mechanics and electrodynamics. Indeed, on Newtonian mechanics, no system of point charges admits of a stable static equilibrium, and any motion of the electrons around the nucleus would, according to Maxwell's electrodynamics, give rise to a dissipation of energy through radiation accompanied by a steady contraction of the system, resulting in the close combination of the nucleus and the electrons within a region of extension far smaller than atomic dimensions.

Still, this situation was not too surprising, since an essential limitation of classical physical theories had already been revealed by Planck's discovery in 1900 of the universal quantum of action which, especially in the hands of Einstein, had found such promising application in the account of specific heats and photochemical reactions. Quite independent of the new experimental evidence as regards the structure of the atom, there was therefore a widespread expectation that quantum concepts might have a decisive bearing on the whole problem of the atomic constitution of matter.

Thus, as I later learned, A. Haas had in 1910 attempted, on the basis of Thomson's atomic model, to fix dimensions and periods of electronic motions by means of Planck's relation between the energy and the frequency of a harmonic oscillator. Further, J. Nicholson had in 1912 made use of quantized angular momenta in his search for the origin of certain lines in the spectra of stellar nebulae and the solar corona. Above all, however, it deserves mention that, following early ideas of Nernst about quantized rotations of molecules, N. Bjerrum already in 1912 predicted the band structure of infra-red absorption lines in diatomic gases, and thereby made a first step towards the detailed analysis of molecular spectra eventually achieved on the basis of the subsequent interpretation, by quantum theory, of the general spectral combination law.

Early in my stay in Manchester in the spring of 1912 I became convinced that the electronic constitution of the Rutherford atom was governed throughout by the quantum of action. A support for this view was found not only in the fact that Planck's relation appeared approximately applicable to the more loosely bound electrons involved in the chemical and optical properties of the elements, but especially in the tracing of similar relationships as regards the most firmly bound electrons in the atom revealed by the characteristic penetrating radiation discovered by Barkla. Thus, measurements of the energy necessary to produce the Barkla radiation by electron bombardment of various elements, performed by Whiddington at the time when I was staying in Cambridge, exhibited simple regularities of the kind to be expected from an estimate of the firmest binding energy of an electron rotating in a Planck orbit round a nucleus with a charge given by the atomic number. From Lawrence Bragg's recently published Rutherford Lecture I have been very interested to learn that William Bragg, then in Leeds, in his first investigation of X-ray spectra, based on Laue's discovery in 1912, was fully aware of the bearing of Whiddington's results on the connection between the Barkla radiation and the ordering of the elements in Mendeleev's table, a problem which through Moseley's work in Manchester soon was to receive such complete elucidation.

During the last month of my stay in Manchester I was mainly occupied with a theoretical investigation of the stopping power of matter for α- and β-rays. This problem, which originally was discussed by J. J. Thomson from the point of view of his own atomic model, had just been re-examined by Darwin on the basis of the Rutherford model. In connection with the considerations mentioned above regarding the frequencies involved in the electron binding in the atom, it occurred to me that the transfer of energy from the particles to the electrons could be simply treated in analogy to the dispersion and absorption of radiation. In this way, it proved possible to interpret the results of the stopping power measurements as additional support for ascribing to hydrogen and helium the atomic numbers 1 and 2 in conformity with general chemical evidence, and in particular with Rutherford and Royds' demonstration of the formation of helium gas by the collection of α-particles escaping from thin-walled emanation tubes. Also for the more complex case of heavier substances, approximate agreement was ascertained with the expected atomic numbers and the estimated values for the binding energies of the electrons, but the theoretical methods were much too primitive to yield more accurate results. As is well known, an appropriate treatment of the problem by modern methods of quantum mechanics was first achieved in 1930 by H. Bethe.

Although Rutherford just at that time was concentrating on the preparation of his great book, *Radioactive Substances and Their Radiations*, he nevertheless followed my work with a constant interest, which gave me the opportunity to learn about the care which he always took in the publications of his pupils. After my return to Denmark I was married in mid-summer 1912 and, on our wedding trip in August to England and Scotland, my wife and I passed through Manchester to visit Rutherford and deliver the completed manuscript of my paper on the stopping problems. Both Rutherford and his wife received us with a cordiality which laid the foundation of the intimate friendship that through the many years connected the families.

II

After settling down in Copenhagen, I remained in close contact with Rutherford, to whom I regularly reported about the development of the work on general atomic problems, which I had started in Manchester. Common to Rutherford's answers, which were always very encouraging, was the spontaneity and joy with which he told about the work in his laboratory. It was indeed the beginning of a long correspondence which lasted over 25 years and which revives, every time I look into it, my memories of Rutherford's enthusiasm for the progress in the field he had opened up and the warm interest he took in the endeavours of everyone trying to contribute to it.

My letters to Rutherford in the autumn of 1912 concerned the continued endeavours to trace the role of the quantum of action for the electronic constitution of the Rutherford atom, including problems of molecular bindings and radiative and magnetic effects. Still, the stability question presented in all such considerations intricate difficulties stimulating the search for a firmer hold. However, after various attempts to apply quantum ideas in a more consistent manner, it struck me in the early spring of 1913 that a clue to the problem of atomic stability directly applicable to the Rutherford atom was offered by the remarkably simple laws governing the optical spectra of the elements.

On the basis of the extremely accurate measurements of the wavelengths of spectral lines by Rowland and others, and after contributions by Balmer and by Schuster, Rutherford's predecessor in the Manchester Chair, the general spectral laws were most ingeniously clarified by Rydberg. The principal result of the thorough analysis of the conspicuous series in the line spectra and their mutual relationship was the recognition that the frequency v of every line in the spectrum of a given element could be represented with unparalleled accuracy as $v = T' - T''$, where T' and T'' are two among a multitude of spectral terms T characteristic of the element.

This fundamental combination law obviously defied ordinary mechanical interpretation, and it is interesting to recall how in this connection Lord Rayleigh had pertinently stressed that any general relationship between the frequencies of the normal modes of vibration of a mechanical model would be quadratic and not linear in these frequencies. For the Rutherford atom we should not even expect a line spectrum, since, according to ordinary electrodynamics, the frequencies of radiation accompanying the electronic motion would change continuously with the energy emitted. It was therefore natural to attempt to base the explanation of spectra directly on the combination law.

In fact, accepting Einstein's idea of light quanta or photons with energy hv, where h is Planck's constant, one was led to assume that any emission or absorption of radiation by the atom is an individual process accompanied by an energy transfer $h(T' - T'')$, and to interpret hT as the binding energy of the electrons in some stable, or so-called stationary, state of the atom. In particular, this assumption offered an immediate explanation of the apparently capricious appearance of emission and absorption lines in series spectra. Thus, in emission processes we witness the transition of the atom from a higher to a lower energy level, whereas in the absorption processes we have in general to do with a transfer of the atom from the ground state, with the lowest energy, to one of its excited states.

In the simplest case of the hydrogen spectrum, the terms are with great accuracy given by $T_n = R/n^2$, where n is an integer and R the Rydberg constant. Thus, the interpretation indicated led to a sequence of decreasing values for the binding energy of the electron in the hydrogen atom, pointing to a steplike process by which the electron, originally at a large distance from the nucleus, passes by radiative transitions to stationary states of firmer and firmer binding, characterized by lower and lower n-values, until the ground state, specified by $n = 1$, is reached. Moreover, a comparison of the binding energy in this state with that of an electron moving in a Keplerian orbit around the nucleus yielded orbital dimensions of the same order as the atomic sizes derived from the properties of gases.

On the basis of the Rutherford atomic model, this view also immediately suggested an explanation of the appearance of the Rydberg constant in the more complex spectra of other elements. Thus, it was concluded that we were here faced with transition processes involving excited states of the atom, in which one of the electrons has been brought outside the region occupied by the other electrons bound to the nucleus, and therefore exposed to a field of force resembling that surrounding a unit charge.

The tracing of a closer relation between the Rutherford atomic model and the spectral evidence obviously presented intricate problems. On the one hand, the very definition of the charge and mass of the electron and the nucleus rested entirely on an analysis of physical phenomena in terms of the principles of classical mechanics and electromagnetism. On the other hand, the so-called quantum postulate, stating that any change of the intrinsic energy of the atom consists in a complete transition between two stationary states, excluded the possibility of accounting on classical principles for the radiative processes or any other reaction involving the stability of the atom.

As we know today, the solution of such problems demanded the development of a mathematical formalism, the proper interpretation of which implied a radical revision of the foundation for the unambiguous use of elementary physical concepts and the recognition of complementary relationships between phenomena observed under different experimental conditions. Still, at that time, some progress could be made by utilizing classical physical pictures for the classification of stationary states based on Planck's original assumptions regarding the energy states of a harmonic oscillator. In particular, a starting point was offered by the closer comparison between an oscillator of given frequency and the Keplerian motion of an electron around a nucleus, with a frequency of revolution depending on the binding energy.

In fact, just as in the case of a harmonic oscillator, a simple calculation showed that, for each of the stationary states of the hydrogen atom, the action integrated over an orbital period of the electron could be identified with nh, a condition which in the case of circular orbits is equivalent to a quantization of the angular momentum in units $h/2\pi$.

Such identification involved a fixation of the Rydberg constant in terms of the charge e and mass m of the electron and Planck's constant, according to the formula

$$R = \frac{2\pi^2 m e^4}{h^3}$$

which was found to agree with the empirical value within the accuracy of the available measurements of e, m and h.

Although this agreement offered an indication of the scope for the use of mechanical models in picturing stationary states, of course the difficulties involved in any combination of quantum ideas and the principles of ordinary mechanics remained. It was therefore most reassuring to find that the whole approach to the spectral problems fulfilled the obvious demand of embracing the classical physical description in the limit where the action involved is sufficiently large to permit the neglect of the individual quantum. Such considerations presented indeed the first indication of the so-called correspondence principle expressing the aim of representing the essentially statistical account of quantum physics as a rational generalization of the classical physical description.

Thus, in ordinary electrodynamics, the composition of the radiation emitted from an electron system should be determined by the frequencies and amplitudes of the harmonic oscillations into which the motion of the system can be resolved. Of course, no such simple relation holds between the Keplerian motion of an electron around a heavy nucleus and the radiation emitted by transitions between the stationary states of the system. However, in the limiting case of transitions between states for which the values of the quantum number n are large compared with their difference, it could be shown that the frequencies of the components of the radiation, appearing as the result of the random individual transition processes, coincide asymptotically with those of the harmonic components of the electron motion. Moreover, the fact that in a Keplerian orbit, in contrast to a simple harmonic oscillation, there appears not only the frequency of revolution but also higher harmonics, offered the possibility of tracing a classical analogy as regards the unrestricted combination of the terms in the hydrogen spectrum.

Still, the unambiguous demonstration of the relation between the Rutherford atomic model and the spectral evidence was for a time hindered by a peculiar circumstance. Already twenty years before, Pickering had observed in the spectra of distant stars a series of lines with wavelengths exhibiting a close numerical relationship with the

D

ordinary hydrogen spectrum. These lines were therefore generally ascribed to hydrogen and were even thought by Rydberg to remove the apparent contrast between the simplicity of the hydrogen spectrum and the complexity of the spectra of other elements, including those of the alkalis, whose structure comes nearest to the hydrogen spectrum. This view was also upheld by the eminent spectroscopist A. Fowler, who just at that time in laboratory experiments with discharges through a mixture of hydrogen and helium gas had observed the Pickering lines and new related spectral series.

However, the Pickering and Fowler lines could not be included in the Rydberg formula for the hydrogen spectrum, unless the number n in the expression for the spectral terms were allowed to take half integrals as well as integral values; but this assumption would evidently destroy the asymptotic approach to the classical relationship between energy and spectral frequencies. On the other hand, such correspondence would hold for the spectrum of a system consisting of an electron bound to a nucleus of charge Ze, whose stationary states are determined by the same value nh of the action integral. Indeed, the spectral terms for such a system would be given by Z^2R/n^2, which for $Z = 2$ yields the same result as the introduction of half-integral values of n in the Rydberg formula. Thus, it was natural to ascribe the Pickering and Fowler lines to helium ionized by the high thermal agitation in the stars and in the strong discharges used by Fowler. Indeed, if this conclusion were confirmed, a first step would have been made towards the establishment of quantitative relationships between the properties of different elements on the basis of the Rutherford model.

III

When in March, 1913, I wrote to Rutherford, enclosing a draft of my first paper on the quantum theory of atomic constitution, I stressed the importance of settling the question of the origin of the Pickering lines and took the opportunity of asking whether experiments to that purpose could be performed in his laboratory, where from Schuster's days appropriate spectroscopic apparatus was available. I received a prompt answer, so characteristic of Rutherford's acute scientific judgment and helpful human attitude, that I shall quote it in full:

March 20, 1913.
Dear Dr. Bohr,
  I have received your paper safely and read it with great interest, but I want to look over it again carefully when I have more leisure. Your ideas as to the mode of origin of the spectrum of hydrogen are very ingenious and seem

to work out well; but the mixture of Planck's ideas with the old mechanics make it very difficult to form a physical idea of what is the basis of it. There appears to me one grave difficulty in your hypothesis, which I have no doubt you fully realise, namely, how does an electron decide what frequency it is going to vibrate at when it passes from one stationary state to the other? It seems to me that you would have to assume that the electron knows beforehand where it is going to stop.

There is one criticism of minor character which I would make in the arrangement of the paper. I think in your endeavour to be clear you have a tendency to make your papers much too long, and a tendency to repeat your statements in different parts of the paper. I think that your paper really ought to be cut down, and I think this could be done without sacrificing anything to clearness. I do not know if you appreciate the fact that long papers have a way of frightening readers, who feel that they have not time to dip into them.

I will go over your paper very carefully and let you know what I think about the details. I shall be quite pleased to send it to the *Phil. Mag.* but I would be happier if its volume could be cut down to a fair amount. In any case I will make any corrections in English that are necessary.

I shall be very pleased to see your later papers, but please take to heart my advice, and try to make them as brief as possible consistent with clearness. I am glad to hear that you are coming over to England later and we shall be very glad to see you when you come to Manchester.

By the way, I was much interested in your speculations in regard to Fowler's spectrum. I mentioned the matter to Evans here, who told me that he was much interested in it, and I think it quite possible that he may try some experiments on the matter when he comes back next term. General work goes well, but I am held up momentarily by finding that the mass of the α-particle comes out rather bigger than it ought to be. If correct it is such an important conclusion that I cannot publish it until I am certain of my accuracy at every point. The experiments take a good deal of time and have to be done with great accuracy.

Yours very sincerely,
E. RUTHERFORD.

P.S. I suppose you have no objection to my using my judgment to cut out any matter I may consider unnecessary in your paper? Please reply.

Rutherford's first remark was certainly very pertinent, touching on a point which was to become a central issue in the subsequent pro-longed discussions. My own views at that time, as expressed in a lecture at a meeting of the Danish Physical Society in October, 1913, were that just the radical departure from the accustomed demands on physical explanation involved in the quantum postulate should of itself leave sufficient scope for the possibility of achieving in due course the incorporation of the new assumptions in a logically consistent scheme. In connection with Rutherford's remark, it is of special interest to recall that Einstein, in his famous paper of 1917 on the derivation of Planck's formula for temperature radiation, took the same starting point as regards the origin of spectra, and pointed to the analogy between the statistical laws governing the occurrence of spontaneous radiation processes and the fundamental law of radioactive decay, formulated by Rutherford and Soddy already in 1903. Indeed, this law, which allowed them at one stroke to disentangle the multifarious phenomena of natural radioactivity then known, also proved the clue to the understanding of the later observed peculiar branching in spontaneous decay processes.

The second point raised with such emphasis in Rutherford's letter brought me into a quite embarrassing situation. In fact, a few days before receiving his answer I had sent Rutherford a considerably extended version of the earlier manuscript, the additions especially concerning the relation between emission and absorption spectra and the asymptotic correspondence with the classical physical theories. I therefore felt the only way to straighten matters was to go at once to Manchester and talk it all over with Rutherford himself. Although Rutherford was as busy as ever, he showed an almost angelic patience with me, and after discussions through several long evenings, during which he declared he had never thought I should prove so obstinate, he consented to leave all the old and new points in the final paper. Surely, both style and language were essentially improved by Rutherford's help and advice, and I have often had occasion to think how right he was in objecting to the rather complicated presentation and especially to the many repetitions caused by reference to previous literature. This Rutherford Memorial Lecture has therefore offered a welcome opportunity to give a more concise account of the actual development of the arguments in those years.

During the following months the discussion about the origin of the spectral lines ascribed to helium ions took a dramatic turn. In the first place, Evans was able to produce the Fowler lines in discharges through helium of extreme purity, not showing any trace of the ordinary hydrogen lines. Still, Fowler was not yet convinced and stressed the spurious manner in which spectra may appear in gas mixtures. Above all, he noted that his accurate measurements of the wavelengths of the Pickering lines did not exactly coincide with those calculated from my formula with $Z = 2$. An answer to the last point was, however, easily found, since it was evident that the mass m in the expression for the Rydberg constant had to be taken not as the mass of a free electron but as the so-called reduced mass $mM(m + M)^{-1}$, where M is the mass of the nucleus. Indeed, taking this correction into account, the predicted relationship between the spectra of hydrogen and ionized helium was in complete agreement with all the measurements. This result was at once welcomed by Fowler, who took the opportunity of pointing out that, also in the spectra of other elements, series were observed in which the ordinary Rydberg constant had to be multiplied by a number close to four. Such series spectra, which are generally referred to as spark spectra, could now be recognized as originating from excited ions in contrast to the so-called arc spectra due to excited neutral atoms.

Continued spectroscopical investigations were in the following years to reveal many spectra of atoms, from which not only one but even several electrons were removed. In particular, the well-known investigations of Bowen led to the recognition that the origin of the nebular spectra discussed by Nicholson had to be sought not in new hypothetical elements, but in atoms of oxygen and nitrogen in a highly ionized state. Eventually, the prospect arose of arriving, by analysis of the processes by which the electrons one by one are bound to the nucleus, at a survey of the binding of every electron in the ground state of the Rutherford atom. In 1913, of course, the experimental evidence was still far too scarce, and the theoretical methods for classification of stationary states were not yet sufficiently developed to cope with so ambitious a task.

IV

In the meantime, the work on the electronic constitution of the atom gradually proceeded, and soon again I permitted myself to ask Rutherford for help and advice. Thus, in June, 1913, I went to Manchester with a second paper which, besides a continued discussion of the radioactive displacement law and the origin of the Barkla radiation, dealt with the ground state of atoms containing several electrons. As regards this problem, I tried tentatively to arrange the electron orbits in closed rings resembling the shell structure originally introduced by J. J. Thomson in his early attempt to account by his atomic model for the periodicity features in Mendeleev's table of the elements.

In Rutherford's laboratory, I met on that occasion Hevesy and Paneth, who told me of the success of the first systematic investigations by the tracer method of the solubility of lead sulphide and chromate, which at the beginning of that year they had carried out together in Vienna. In every way, these repeated visits to Manchester were a great stimulation and gave me the welcome opportunity to keep abreast of the work in the laboratory. At that time, assisted by Robinson, Rutherford was busily engaged in the analysis of β-ray emission and, in cooperation with Andrade, studied γ-ray spectra. Moreover, Darwin and Moseley were then intensely occupied with refined theoretical and experimental investigations on the diffraction of X-rays in crystals.

A special opportunity to see Rutherford again soon arose in connection with the meeting of the British Association for the Advancement of Science in Birmingham in September, 1913. At the meeting, attended by Madame Curie, there was in particular a general discussion about the problem of radiation with the participation of such authorities as Rayleigh, Larmor and Lorentz, and especially Jeans, who gave an introductory survey of the application of quantum theory to the problem of atomic constitution. His lucid exposition was, in fact, the first public expression of serious interest in considerations which outside the Manchester group were generally received with much scepticism.

An incident which amused Rutherford and us all was the remark of Lord Rayleigh in response to a solemn request by Sir Joseph Larmor to express his opinion on the latest developments. The prompt reply from the great veteran, who in earlier years had contributed so decisively to the elucidation of radiation problems, was: "In my young days I took many views very strongly and among them that a man who has passed his sixtieth year ought not to express himself about modern ideas. Although I must confess that today I do not take this view quite so strongly, I keep it strongly enough not to take part in this discussion!"

On my visit to Manchester in June I had discussed with Darwin and Moseley the question of the proper sequence for the arrangement of the elements according to their atomic number, and learned then for the first time about Moseley's plans to settle this problem by systematic measurements of the high-frequency spectra of the elements by the Laue–Bragg method. With Moseley's extraordinary energy and gifts of purposeful experimentation, his work developed astonishingly quickly, and already in November, 1913, I received a most interesting letter from him with an account of his important results and with some questions regarding their interpretation on the lines which had proved applicable to the optical spectra.

In modern history of physics and chemistry, few events have from the outset attracted such general interest as Moseley's discovery of the simple laws allowing an unambiguous assignment of the atomic number to any element from its high-frequency spectrum. Not only was the decisive support of the Rutherford atomic model immediately recognized, but also the intuition which had led Mendeleev at certain places in his table to depart from the sequence of increasing atomic weights was strikingly brought out. In particular, it was evident that

Moseley's laws offered an unerring guide in the search for as yet un-discovered elements fitting into vacant places in the series of atomic numbers.

Also as regards the problem of the configuration of the electrons in the atom, Moseley's work was to initiate important progress. Cer-tainly, the predominance, in the innermost part of the atom, of the attraction exerted by the nucleus on the individual electrons over their mutual repulsion afforded the basis for an understanding of the striking similarity between Moseley's spectra and those to be expected for a system consisting of a single electron bound to the bare nucleus. The closer comparison, however, brought new information pertaining to the shell structure of the electronic constitution of the atoms.

An important contribution to this problem was soon after given by Kossel, who pointed to the removal of an electron from one of the sequence of rings or shells surrounding the nucleus as the origin of the K, L, and M types of Barkla radiation. In particular, he ascribed the $K\alpha$ and $K\beta$ components of Moseley's spectra to individual transition processes by which the electron lacking in the K-shell is replaced by one of the electrons in the L- and M-shells, respectively. Proceeding in this way, Kossel was able to trace further relationships between Moseley's measurements of the spectral frequencies, which permitted him to represent the whole high-frequency spectrum of an element as a combination scheme in which the product of any of the terms and Planck's constant was to be identified with the energy required to remove an electron from a shell in the atom to a distance from the nucleus beyond all the shells.

In addition, Kossel's views offered an explanation of the fact that the absorption of penetrating radiation of increasing wavelength practically begins with an absorption edge representing the complete removal in one step of an electron of the respective shell. The absence of inter-mediate excited states was assumed to be due to the full occupation of all shells in the ground state of the atom. As is well known, this view eventually found its final expression through Pauli's formulation in 1924 of the general exclusion principle for electron binding states, inspired by Stoner's derivation of finer details of the shell structure of the Rutherford atom from an analysis of the regularities of the optical spectra.

v

In the autumn of 1913, another stir among physicists was created by Stark's discovery of the surprisingly large effect of electric fields on the structure of the lines in the hydrogen spectrum. With his vigilant attention to all progress in physical science, Rutherford, when he had received Stark's paper from the Prussian Academy, at once wrote to me: "I think it is rather up to you at the present time to write something on the Zeeman and electric effects, if it is possible to reconcile them with your theory." Responding to Rutherford's challenge, I tried to look into the matter, and it was soon clear to me that in the effects of electric and magnetic fields we had to do with two very different problems.

The essence of Lorentz' and Larmor's interpretations of Zeeman's famous discovery in 1896 was that it pointed directly to electron motions as the origin of line spectra in a way largely independent of special assumptions about the binding mechanism of the electrons in the atom. Even if the origin of the spectra is assigned to individual transitions between stationary states, the correspondence principle thus led one, in view of Larmor's general theorem, to expect a normal Zeeman effect for all spectral lines emitted by electrons bound in a field of central symmetry, as in the Rutherford atom. Rather did the appearance of so-called anomalous Zeeman effects present new puzzles which could only be overcome more than ten years later when the complex structure of the lines in series spectra was traced to an intrinsic electron spin. A most interesting historical account of this development, to which important contributions were given from various sides, can be found in the well-known volume recently published in memory of Pauli.

In the case of an electric field, however, no effect proportional to its intensity was to be expected for the radiation emitted by a harmonic oscillator, and Stark's discovery therefore definitely excluded the conventional idea of elastic vibrations of electrons as the origin of line spectra. Still, for a Keplerian motion of the electron around the nucleus, even a comparatively weak external electric field will through secular perturbations produce considerable changes in the shape and orientation of the orbit. By the study of particular cases in which the orbit remains purely periodic in the external field it was possible, by arguments of the same type as those applied to the stationary states of the undisturbed hydrogen atom, to deduce the order of magnitude of the Stark effect, and especially to explain its rapid rise from line to line within the hydrogen spectral series. Yet these considerations clearly showed that, for an explanation of the finer details of the phenomenon, the methods for a classification of stationary states of atomic systems were not sufficiently developed.

In just this respect a great advance was achieved in the following years by the introduction of quantum numbers specifying components of angular momenta and other action integrals. Such methods were first suggested by W. Wilson in 1915, who applied them to electron orbits in the hydrogen atom. However, owing to the circumstance that on Newtonian mechanics every orbit in this case is simply periodic, with a frequency of revolution depending only on the total energy of the system, no physical effects were disclosed. Still, the velocity dependence of the electron mass, predicted by the new mechanics of Einstein, removes the degeneracy of the motion and introduces a second period in its harmonic components through a continual slow progression of the aphelion of the Keplerian orbit. In fact, as was shown in Sommerfeld's famous paper of 1916, the separate quantization of the angular momentum and of the action in the radial motion permitted a detailed interpretation of the observed fine structure of the lines in the spectra of the hydrogen atom and helium ion.

Moreover, the effect of magnetic and electric fields on the hydrogen spectrum was treated by Sommerfeld and Epstein, who, by a masterly application of the methods for quantization of multiperiodic systems, were able, in complete accordance with observations, to derive the spectral terms by the combination of which the resolution of the hydrogen lines appears. The compatibility of such methods with the principle of adiabatic invariance of stationary states, which Ehrenfest had formulated in 1914 in order to meet thermodynamical requirements, was secured by the circumstance that the action integrals to which the quantum numbers refer according to classical mechanics are not modified by a variation of the external field slow compared with the characteristic periods of the system.

Further evidence of the fruitfulness of the approach was derived from the application of the correspondence principle to the radiation emitted by multiperiodic systems, permitting qualitative conclusions regarding the relative probabilities for the different transition processes. These considerations were not least confirmed by Kramers' explanation of the apparently capricious variations in the intensities of the Stark effect components of the hydrogen lines. It was even found possible to account by the correspondence argument for the absence of certain types of transitions in other atoms, beyond those which, as pointed out by Rubinowicz, could be excluded by the conservation laws for energy and angular momentum applied to the reaction between the atom and the radiation.

With the help of the rapidly increasing experimental evidence about the structure of complicated optical spectra, as well as the methodical search for finer regularities in the high-frequency spectra by Siegbahn and his collaborators, the classification of the binding states in atoms containing several electrons continually advanced. In particular, the study of the way in which the ground states of the atoms could be built up by the successive bindings of the electrons to the nucleus led to a gradual elucidation of the shell structure of the electronic configuration in the atom. Thus, although such essential elements of the explanation as the electron spin were still unknown, it became in fact possible within about ten years of Rutherford's discovery of the atomic nucleus to achieve a summary interpretation of many of the most striking periodicity features of Mendeleev's table.

The whole approach, however, was still of largely semi-empirical character, and it was soon to become clear that, for an exhaustive account of the physical and chemical properties of the elements, a radically new departure from classical mechanics was needed in order to incorporate the quantum postulate in a logically consistent scheme. To this well-known development we shall have occasion to return, but I shall first proceed with the account of my reminiscences of Rutherford.

VI

The outbreak of the First World War brought about an almost complete dissolution of the Manchester group, but I was lucky to remain in close contact with Rutherford, who in the spring of 1914 had invited me to succeed Darwin in the Schuster Readership of Mathematical Physics. On our arrival in Manchester in early autumn, after a stormy voyage round Scotland, my wife and I were most kindly received by the few of our old friends who remained in the laboratory after the departure of colleagues from abroad and the participation in military duties by most of the British. Rutherford and his wife were at that time still in America on their way back from a visit to their relatives in New Zealand, and it goes without saying that their safe return to Manchester some weeks later was greeted by all of us with great relief and joy.

Rutherford was himself soon drawn into military projects, especially concerning the development of methods of sound tracing of submarines, and teaching the students was almost entirely left to Evans, Makower and me. Still, Rutherford found time to continue his own pioneer work, which already before the end of the war was to give such great results, and showed the same warm interest as ever in the endeavours of his collaborators. As regards the problem of atomic constitution, a new impulse was given by the publication in 1914 of the famous experiments by Franck and Hertz on the excitation of atoms by electron impact.

On the one hand, these experiments, carried out with mercury vapour, gave most conspicuous evidence of the stepwise energy transfer in atomic processes; on the other hand, the value of the ionization energy of mercury atoms apparently indicated by the experiments was less than half of that to be expected from the interpretation of the mercury spectrum. One was therefore led to suspect that the ionization observed was not directly related to the electronic collisions but was due to an accompanying photoeffect on the electrodes, produced by the radiation emitted by the mercury atoms on their return from the first excited state to the ground state. Encouraged by Rutherford, Makower and I planned experiments to investigate this point, and an intricate quartz apparatus with various electrodes and grids was constructed with the help of the competent German glass blower in the laboratory, who in the earlier days had made the fine α-ray tubes for Rutherford's investigations on the formation of helium.

With his liberal human attitude, Rutherford had tried to obtain permission for the glass blower to continue his work in England in the wartime, but the man's temper, not uncommon for artisans in his field, releasing itself in violent super-patriotic utterances, eventually led to his internment by the British authorities. Thus, when our fine apparatus was ruined by an accident in which its support caught fire, there was no help to reconstruct it, and when also Makower shortly afterwards volunteered for military service, the experiments were given up. I need hardly add that the problem was solved with the expected result quite independently by the brilliant investigations of Davis and Gauthier in New York in 1918, and I have only mentioned our fruitless attempts as an indication of the kind of difficulties with which work in the Manchester laboratory was faced in those days, and which were very similar to those the ladies had to cope with in their households.

Still, Rutherford's never-failing optimism exerted a most encouraging influence on his surroundings, and I remember how at the time of a serious set-back in the war, Rutherford quoted the old utterance ascribed to Napoleon about the impossibility of fighting the British because they were too stupid to understand when they had lost. To me, it was also a most pleasant and enlightening experience to be admitted to the monthly discussions among a group of Rutherford's personal friends, including Alexander, the philosopher, the historian Tout, the anthropologist Elliot Smith, and Chaim Weizmann, the chemist, who thirty years later was to become the first president of Israel and for whose distinctive personality Rutherford had great esteem.

A terrible shock to us all was the tragic message in 1915 of Moseley's untimely death in the Gallipoli campaign, deplored so deeply by the community of physicists all over the world, and which not least Rutherford, who had endeavoured to get Moseley transferred from the front to less dangerous duties, took much to heart.

In the summer of 1916 my wife and I left Manchester and returned to Denmark, where I had been appointed to the newly created professorship of theoretical physics in the University of Copenhagen. Notwithstanding the ever-increasing difficulties of postal communication, a steady correspondence with Rutherford was kept up. From my side, I reported about the progress with the work on a more general representation of the quantum theory of atomic constitution which at that time was further stimulated by the development as regards the classification of stationary states, already referred to. In that connection, Rutherford took an interest in what news I could give from the Continent, and in particular of my first personal contact with Sommerfeld and Ehrenfest. In his own letters, Rutherford also gave a vivid description of how, in spite of the increasing difficulties and the pressure of other obligations, he strove to continue his investigations in various directions. Thus, in the autumn of 1916, Rutherford wrote about his intense interest in some surprising results regarding the absorption of hard γ-rays produced by high-voltage tubes which had just then become available.

In the next years Rutherford was more and more occupied with the possibilities of producing nuclear disintegrations by means of fast α-rays, and already in a letter on December 9th, 1917, he writes:

I occasionally find an odd half day to try a few of my own experiments and have got I think results that will ultimately prove of great importance. I wish you were here to talk matters over with. I am detecting and counting the lighter atoms set in motion by α-particles, and the results, I think, throw a good deal of light on the character and distribution of forces near the nucleus. I am also trying to break up the atom by this method. In one case, the results look promising but a great deal of work will be required to make sure. Kay helps me and is now an expert counter.

A year later, November 17th, 1918, Rutherford in his characteristic manner announced further progress:

I wish I had you here to discuss the meaning of some of my results in collision of nuclei. I have got some rather startling results, I think, but it is a heavy and long business getting *certain* proofs of my deductions. Counting weak scintillations is hard on old eyes, but still with the aid of Kay I have got through a good deal of work at odd times the past four years.

In Rutherford's famous papers in the *Philosophical Magazine*, 1919, containing the account of his fundamental discovery of controlled nuclear disintegrations, he refers to the visit to Manchester, in November, 1918, of his old collaborator Ernest Marsden, who at the Armistice had got leave from military service in France. With his great experience of scintillation experiments from the old Manchester days when, in collaboration with Geiger, he performed the experiments which led Rutherford to his discovery of the atomic nucleus, Marsden helped him to clear up some apparent anomalies in the statistical distribution of the high-speed protons released by the bombardment of nitrogen with α-rays. From Manchester, Marsden returned to New Zealand to take up his own university duties, but kept in close contact with Rutherford through the years.

In July, 1919, when after the Armistice travelling was again possible, I went to Manchester to see Rutherford and learned in more detail about his great new discovery of controlled, or so-called artificial, nuclear transmutations, by which he gave birth to what he liked to call "modern Alchemy", and which in the course of time was to give rise to such tremendous consequences as regards man's mastery of the forces of nature. Rutherford was at that time almost alone in the laboratory, and as told in his letters, the only help in his fundamental researches, apart from Marsden's short visit, was his faithful assistant William Kay, who by his kindness and helpfulness through the years had endeared himself to everyone in the laboratory. During my visit Rutherford also spoke about the great decision he had had to make in response to the offer of the Cavendish professorship in Cambridge left vacant by the retirement of J. J. Thomson. Certainly, it had not been easy for Rutherford to decide to leave Manchester after the many rich years there, but of course he had to follow the call to succeed the unique series of Cavendish professors.

VII

From the beginning, Rutherford gathered around him in the Cavendish Laboratory a large and brilliant group of research workers. A most notable figure was Aston, who through many years had worked with J. J. Thomson and already during the wartime had started the development of mass spectroscopic methods which was to lead to the demonstration of the existence of isotopes of almost every element. This discovery, which gave such a convincing confirmation of Rutherford's atomic model, was not entirely unexpected. Already in the early Manchester days, it was understood that the apparent irregularities in the sequence of the atomic weights of the elements when they were ordered according to their chemical properties suggested that, even for the stable elements, the nuclear charge could not be expected to have a unique relation to the nuclear mass. In letters to me in January and February, 1920, Rutherford expressed his joy in Aston's work, particularly about the chlorine isotopes which so clearly illustrated the statistical character of the deviations of chemical atomic weights from integral values. He also commented humorously on the lively disputes in the Cavendish Laboratory about the relative merits of different atomic models to which Aston's discovery gave rise.

It was a great help in the continuation of Rutherford's own pioneering work on the constitution and disintegrations of atomic nuclei as well as in the management of the great laboratory, that from the very beginning he was joined by James Chadwick from the old Manchester group, who returned from a long detention in Germany, where at the outbreak of the war he had been working in Berlin with Geiger. Among Rutherford's collaborators in the early Cambridge years were also Blackett and Ellis, both coming from a career in the defence services, Ellis having been initiated to physics by Chadwick during their comradeship under German imprisonment. A further asset to the group at the Cavendish was the arrival, a few years later, of Kapitza, who brought with him ingenious projects, in particular for the production of magnetic fields of hitherto unheard-of intensities. In this work he was from the start assisted by John Cockcroft, who with his singular combination of scientific and technological insight was to become such a prominent collaborator of Rutherford.

At the beginning, Charles Darwin, whose mathematical insight had been so helpful in the Manchester years, shared with Ralph Fowler responsibility for the theoretical part of the activities at the Cavendish. In collaboration, they made at that time important contributions to statistical thermodynamics and its application to astrophysical problems. After Darwin's departure for Edinburgh, the principal theoretical adviser and teacher in Cambridge right up to the Second World War was Fowler, who had become Rutherford's son-in-law. Not only did Fowler with enthusiastic vigour participate in the work at the Cavendish, but he also soon found numerous gifted pupils who benefited from his inspiration. Foremost among these were Lennard-Jones and Hartree, who both contributed, each along his own line, to the development of atomic and molecular physics, and especially Dirac, who from his early youth distinguished himself by his unique logical power.

Ever since I left Manchester in 1916, I had, of course, tried to use the experience gained in Rutherford's laboratory, and it is with gratitude that I recall how Rutherford from the very outset most kindly and effectively supported my endeavours in Copenhagen to create an institute to promote intimate collaboration between theoretical and experimental physicists. It was a special encouragement that already in the autumn of 1920, when the Institute building was nearing completion, Rutherford found time to visit us in Copenhagen. As a token of appreciation, the University conferred upon him an honorary degree, and on that occasion he gave a most stimulating and humorous address which was long remembered by all present.

For the work in the new Institute it was of great benefit that we were joined shortly after the war by my old friend from the Manchester days, George Hevesy, who during the more than twenty years he worked in Copenhagen carried out many of his famous physico-chemical and biological researches, based on the isotopic tracer method. A special event, in which Rutherford took great interest, was the application of Moseley's method by Coster and Hevesy in 1922 to the successful search for the missing element now called hafnium, the properties of which gave strong additional support to the interpretation of the periodic system of the elements. An auspicious start was given to the general experimental work by a visit, at the opening of the laboratory, of James Franck, who during the following months most kindly instructed the Danish collaborators in the refined technique of excitation of atomic spectra by electron bombardment, which he had so ingeniously developed together with Gustav Hertz. The first among the many distinguished theoretical physicists who stayed with us for a longer period was Hans Kramers, who as a quite young man came to Copenhagen during the war and proved to be such an invaluable asset to our group during the ten years he worked with us until, in 1926, he left his position as lecturer in the Institute to take over a professorship in Utrecht. Shortly after Kramers' arrival in Copenhagen came two promising young men, Oscar Klein from Sweden and Svein Rosseland from Norway, who already in 1920 made their names known by pointing to the so-called collisions of the second kind, in which atoms are transferred by electron bombardment from a higher to a lower stationary state with gain of velocity for the electron. Indeed, the occurrence of such processes is decisive for ensuring thermal equilibrium in a way analogous to the induced radiative transitions which played an essential role in Einstein's derivation of Planck's formula for temperature radiation. The consideration of collisions of the second kind proved particularly important for the elucidation of the radiative properties of stellar atmospheres, to which at that time Saha, working in Cambridge with Fowler, made such fundamental contributions.

The group at the Copenhagen Institute was joined in 1922 by Pauli, and two years later by Heisenberg, both pupils of Sommerfeld, and who, young as they were, had already accomplished most brilliant work. I had made their acquaintance and formed a deep impression of their extraordinary talent in the summer of 1922 during a lecturing visit to Göttingen, which initiated a long and fruitful cooperation between the group working there under the leadership of Born and Franck, and the Copenhagen group. From the early days our close connection with the great centre in Cambridge was maintained especially by longer visits to Copenhagen of Darwin, Dirac, Fowler, Hartree, Mott, and others.

VIII

Those years, when a unique cooperation of a whole generation of theoretical physicists from many countries created step by step a logically consistent generalization of classical mechanics and electromagnetism, have sometimes been described as the heroic era in quantum physics. To everyone following this development it was an unforgettable experience to witness how, through the combination of different lines of approach and the introduction of appropriate mathematical methods, a new outlook emerged regarding the comprehension of physical experience. Many obstacles had to be overcome before this goal was reached, and time and again decisive progress was achieved by some of the youngest among us.

The common starting point was the recognition that, notwithstanding the great help which the use of mechanical pictures had temporarily offered for the classification of stationary states of atoms in isolation or exposed to constant external forces, it was clear, as already mentioned, that a fundamentally new departure was needed. Not only was the difficulty of picturing the electronic constitution of chemical compounds on the basis of the Rutherford atomic model more and more evident, but insurmountable difficulties also arose in any attempts to account in detail for the complexity of atomic spectra, especially conspicuous in the peculiar duplex character of the arc spectrum of helium.

The first step to a more general formulation of the correspondence principle was offered by the problem of optical dispersion. Indeed, the close relation between the atomic dispersion and the selective absorption of spectral lines so beautifully illustrated by the ingenious experiments of R. W. Wood and P. V. Bevan on the absorption and dispersion in alkali vapours, suggested from the very beginning a correspondence approach. On the basis of Einstein's formulation of the statistical laws for the occurrence of radiation-induced transitions between stationary states of an atomic system, Kramers in 1924 succeeded in establishing a general dispersion formula, involving only the energies of these states and the probabilities of spontaneous transitions between them. This theory, further developed by Kramers and Heisenberg, included even new dispersion effects connected with the appearance, under the influence of the radiation, of possibilities for transitions not present in the unperturbed atom, and an analogue to which is the Raman effect in molecular spectra.

Shortly afterwards, an advance of fundamental significance was achieved by Heisenberg, who in 1925 introduced a most ingenious formalism, in which all use of orbital pictures beyond the general asymptotic correspondence was avoided. In this bold conception the canonical equations of mechanics are retained in their Hamiltonian form, but the conjugate variables are replaced by operators subject to a non-commutative algorism involving Planck's constant as well as the symbol $\sqrt{-1}$. In fact, by representing the mechanical quantities by hermitian matrices with elements referring to all possible transition processes between stationary states, it proved possible without any arbitrariness to deduce the energies of these states and the probabilities of the associated transition processes. This so-called quantum mechanics, to the elaboration of which Born and Jordan as well as Dirac from the outset made important contributions, opened the way to a consistent statistical treatment of many atomic problems which hitherto were only amenable to a semi-empirical approach.

For the completion of this great task the emphasis on the formal analogy between mechanics and optics, originally stressed by Hamilton, proved most helpful and instructive. Thus, pointing to the similar roles played by the quantum numbers in the classification of stationary states by means of mechanical pictures, and by the numbers of nodes in characterizing the possible standing waves in elastic media, L. de Broglie had already in 1924 been led to a comparison between the behaviour of free material particles and the properties of photons. Especially illuminating was his demonstration of the identity of the particle velocity with the group velocity of a wave-packet built up of components with wavelengths confined to a small interval, and each related to a value of the momentum by Einstein's equation between the momentum of a photon and the corresponding wavelength of radiation. As is well known, the pertinence of this comparison soon received a decisive confirmation with the discoveries by Davisson and Germer and by George Thomson of selective scattering of electrons in crystals.

E

The culminating event of this period was Schrödinger's establishment in 1926 of a more comprehensive wave mechanics in which the stationary states are conceived as proper solutions of a fundamental wave equation, obtained by regarding the Hamiltonian of a system of electric particles as a differential operator acting upon a function of the coordinates which define the configuration of the system. In the case of the hydrogen atom, not only did this method lead to a remarkably simple determination of the energies of the stationary states, but Schrödinger also showed that the superposition of any two proper solutions corresponded to a distribution of electric charge and current in the atom, which on classical electrodynamics would give rise to the emission and resonance absorption of a monochromatic radiation of a frequency coinciding with some line of the hydrogen spectrum.

Similarly, Schrödinger was able to explain essential features of the dispersion of radiation by atoms by representing the charge and current distribution of the atom perturbed by the incident radiation as the effect of a superposition of the proper functions defining the manifold of possible stationary states of the unperturbed system. Particularly suggestive was the derivation on such lines of the laws of the Compton effect, which, in spite of the striking support it gave to Einstein's original photon idea, at first presented obvious difficulties for a correspondence treatment, attempting to combine conservation of energy and momentum with a division of the process in two separate steps, consisting in an absorption and an emission of radiation resembling radiative transitions between the stationary states of an atomic system.

This recognition of the wide scope of arguments implying the use of a superposition principle similar to that of classical electromagnetic field theory, which was only implicitly contained in the matrix formulation of quantum mechanics, meant a great advance in the treatment of atomic problems. Still, it was from the beginning obvious that wave mechanics did not point to any less radical modification of the classical physical approach than the statistical description envisaged by the correspondence principle. Thus, I remember how, on a visit of Schrödinger to Copenhagen in 1926, when he gave us a most impressive account of his wonderful work, we argued with him that any procedure disregarding the individual character of the quantum processes would never account for Planck's fundamental formula of thermal radiation.

Notwithstanding the remarkable analogy between essential features of atomic processes and classical resonance problems, it must indeed be taken into account that in wave mechanics we are dealing with functions which do not generally take real values, but demand the essential use of the symbol $\sqrt{-1}$ just as the matrices of quantum mechanics. Moreover, when dealing with the constitution of atoms with more than one electron, or collisions between atoms and free electric particles, the state functions are not represented in ordinary space but in a configuration space of as many dimensions as there are degrees of freedom in the total system. The essentially statistical character of the physical deductions from wave mechanics was eventually clarified by Born's brilliant treatment of general collision problems.

The equivalence of the physical contents of the two different mathematical formalisms was completely elucidated by the transformation theory formulated independently by Dirac in Copenhagen, and Jordan in Göttingen, which introduced in quantum physics possibilities for the change of variables similar to those offered by the symmetrical character of the equations of motion in classical dynamics in the canonical form given by Hamilton. An analogous situation is met with in the formulation of a quantum electrodynamics incorporating the photon concept. This aim was first achieved in Dirac's quantum theory of radiation treating phases and amplitudes of the harmonic components of the fields as non-commuting variables. After further ingenious contributions by Jordan, Klein, and Wigner, this formalism found, as is well known, essential completion in the work of Heisenberg and Pauli.

A special illustration of the power and scope of the mathematical methods of quantum physics is presented by the peculiar quantum statistics pertaining to systems of identical particles where we have to do with a feature as foreign to classical physics as the quantum of action itself. Indeed, any problem which calls for relevant application of Bose–Einstein or Fermi–Dirac statistics in principle excludes pictorial illustration. In particular, this situation left room for the proper formulation of the Pauli exclusion principle, which not only gave the final elucidation of the periodicity relations in Mendeleev's table, but in the following years proved fertile for the understanding of most of the varied aspects of the atomic constitution of matter.

A fundamental contribution to the clarification of the principles of quantum statistics was afforded by Heisenberg's ingenious explanation in 1926 of the duplicity of the helium spectrum. In fact, as he showed, the set of stationary states of atoms with two electrons consists of two non-combining groups corresponding to symmetric and antisymmetric spatial wave functions, respectively associated with opposite and parallel orientations of the electron spins. Shortly afterwards, Heitler and London succeeded on the same lines in explaining the binding mechanism in the hydrogen molecule and thereby opened the way for the understanding of homopolar chemical bonds. Even Rutherford's famous formula for the scattering of charged particles by atomic nuclei had, as was shown by Mott, to be essentially modified when applied to collisions between identical particles like protons and hydrogen nuclei or α-rays and helium nuclei. However, in the actual experiments of large angle scattering of fast α-rays by heavy nuclei, from which Rutherford drew his fundamental conclusions, we are well within the range of validity of classical mechanics.

The increasing use of more and more refined mathematical abstractions to ensure consistency in the account of atomic phenomena found in 1928 a temporary climax in Dirac's relativistic quantum theory of the electron. Thus, the concept of electron spin, to the treatment of which Darwin and Pauli had made important contributions, was harmoniously incorporated in Dirac's spinor analysis. Above all, however, in connection with the discovery of the positron by Anderson and Blackett, Dirac's theory prepared the recognition of the existence of antiparticles of equal mass by opposite electric charges and opposite orientations of the magnetic moment relative to the spin axis. As is well known, we have here to do with a development which in a novel manner has restored and enlarged that isotropy in space and reversibility in time which has been one of the basic ideas of the classical physical approach.

The wonderful progress of our knowledge of the atomic constitution of matter and of the methods by which such knowledge can be acquired and interrelated has indeed carried us far beyond the scope of the deterministic pictorial description brought to such perfection by Newton and Maxwell. Following this development at close hand, I have often had occasion to think of the dominating influence of Rutherford's original discovery of the atomic nucleus, which at every stage presented us with so forceful a challenge.

IX

In all the long and rich years during which Rutherford worked with untiring vigour in the Cavendish, I often came to Cambridge, where on Rutherford's invitation I gave several courses of lectures on theoretical problems, including the epistemological implications of the development of quantum theory. On such occasions it was always a great encouragement to feel the open mind and intense interest with which Rutherford followed the progress in the field of research which he had himself so largely initiated and the growth of which should carry us so far beyond the horizon which limited the outlook at the early stages.

Indeed, the extensive use of abstract mathematical methods to cope with the rapidly increasing evidence about atomic phenomena brought the whole observational problem more and more to the foreground. In its roots this problem is as old as physical science itself. Thus, the philosophers in ancient Greece, who based the explanation of the specific properties of substances on the limited divisibility of all matter, took it for granted that the coarseness of our sense organs would for ever prevent the direct observation of individual atoms. In such respect, the situation has been radically changed in our days by the construction of amplification devices such as cloud chambers and the counter mechanisms originally developed by Rutherford and Geiger in connection with their measurements of the numbers and charges of α-particles. Still, the exploration of the world of atoms was, as we have seen, to reveal inherent limitations in the mode of description embodied in common language developed for the orientation in our surroundings and the account of events of daily life.

In words conforming with Rutherford's whole attitude, one may say that the aim of experimentation is to put questions to nature, and of course Rutherford owed his success in this task to his intuition in shaping such questions so as to permit the most useful answers. In order that the inquiry may augment common knowledge, it is an obvious demand that the recording of observations as well as the construction and handling of the apparatus, necessary for the definition of the experimental conditions, be described in plain language. In actual physical research, this demand is amply satisfied with the specification of the experimental arrangement through the use of bodies like diaphragms and photographic plates, so large and heavy that their manipulation can be accounted for in terms of classical physics, although of course the properties of the materials of which the instruments, as well as our own bodies, are built up depend essentially on the constitution and stability of the component atomic systems defying such account.

The description of ordinary experience presupposes the unrestricted divisibility of the course of the phenomena in space and time and the linking of all steps in an unbroken chain in terms of cause and effect. Ultimately, this viewpoint rests on the fineness of our senses, which for perception demands an interaction with the objects under investigation so small that in ordinary circumstances it is without appreciable influence on the course of events. In the edifice of classical physics, this situation finds its idealized expression in the assumption that the interaction between the object and the tools of observation can be neglected or, at any rate, compensated for.

The element of wholeness, symbolized by the quantum of action and completely foreign to classical physical principles has, however, the consequence that in the study of quantum processes any experimental inquiry implies an interaction between the atomic object and the measuring tools which, although essential for the characterization of the phenomena, evades a separate account if the experiment is to serve its purpose of yielding unambiguous answers to our questions. It is indeed the recognition of this situation which makes the recourse to a statistical mode of description imperative as regards the expectations of the occurrence of individual quantum effects in one and the same experimental arrangement, and which removes any apparent contradiction between phenomena observed under mutually exclusive experimental conditions. However contrasting such phenomena may at first appear, it must be realized that they are complementary in the sense that taken together they exhaust all information about the atomic object which can be expressed in common language without ambiguity.

The notion of complementarity does not imply any renunciation of detailed analysis limiting the scope of our inquiry, but simply stresses the character of objective description, independent of subjective judgment, in any field of experience where unambiguous communication essentially involves regard to the circumstances in which evidence is obtained. In logical respect, such a situation is well known from discussions about psychological and social problems where many words have been used in a complementary manner since the very origin of language. Of course we are here often dealing with qualities unsuited to the quantitative analysis characteristic of so-called exact sciences, whose task, according to the programme of Galileo, is to base all description on well-defined measurements.

Notwithstanding the help which mathematics has always offered for such a task, it must be realized that the very definition of mathematical symbols and operations rests on simple logical use of common language. Indeed, mathematics is not to be regarded as a special branch of knowledge based on the accumulation of experience, but rather as a refinement of general language, supplementing it with appropriate tools to represent relations for which ordinary verbal communication is imprecise or too cumbersome. Strictly speaking, the mathematical formalism of quantum mechanics and electrodynamics merely offers rules of calculation for the deduction of expectations about observations obtained under well-defined experimental conditions specified by classical physical concepts. The exhaustive character of this description depends not only on the freedom, offered by the formalism, of choosing these conditions in any conceivable manner, but equally on the fact that the very definition of the phenomena under consideration for their completion implies an element of irreversibility in the observational process emphasizing the fundamentally irreversible character of the concept of observation itself.

Of course, all contradictions in the complementary account in quantum physics were beforehand excluded by the logical consistency of the mathematical scheme upholding every demand of correspondence. Still, the recognition of the reciprocal latitude for the fixation of any two canonically conjugate variables, expressed in the principle of indeterminacy formulated by Heisenberg in 1927, was a decisive step towards the elucidation of the measuring problem in quantum mechanics. Indeed, it became evident that the formal representation of physical quantities by non-commuting operators directly reflects the relationship of mutual exclusion between the operations by which the respective physical quantities are defined and measured.

To gain familiarity with this situation, the detailed treatment of a great variety of examples of such arguments was needed. Notwithstanding the generalized significance of the superposition principle in quantum physics, an important guide for the closer study of observational problems was repeatedly found in Rayleigh's classic analysis of the inverse relation between the accuracy of image-forming by microscopes and the resolving power of spectroscopic instruments. In this connection not least Darwin's mastery of the methods of mathematical physics often proved helpful.

With all appreciation of Planck's happy choice of words when introducing the concept of a universal "quantum of action", or the suggestive value of the idea of "intrinsic spin", it must be realized that such notions merely refer to relationships between well-defined experimental evidence which cannot be comprehended by the classical mode of description. Indeed, the numbers expressing the values of the quantum or spin in ordinary physical units do not concern direct measurements of classically defined actions or angular momenta, but are logically interpretable only by consistent use of the mathematical formalism of quantum theory. In particular, the much discussed impossibility of measuring the magnetic moment of a free electron by ordinary magnetometers is directly evident from the fact that in Dirac's theory the spin and magnetic moment do not result from any alteration in the basic Hamiltonian equation of motion, but appear as consequences of the peculiar non-commutative character of the operator calculus.

The question of the proper interpretation of the notions of complementarity and indeterminacy was not settled without lively disputes, in particular at the Solvay meetings of 1927 and 1930. On these occasions, Einstein challenged us with his subtle criticism which especially gave the inspiration to a closer analysis of the role of the instruments in the measuring process. A crucial point, irrevocably excluding the possibility of reverting to causal pictorial description, was the recognition that the scope of unambiguous application of the general conservation laws of momentum and energy is inherently limited by the circumstance that any experimental arrangement, allowing the location of atomic objects in space and time, implies a transfer, uncontrollable in principle, of momentum and energy to the fixed scales and regulated clocks indispensable for the definition of the reference frame. The physical interpretation of the relativistic formulation of quantum theory ultimately rests on the possibility of fulfilling all relativity exigencies in the account of the handling of the macroscopic measuring apparatus.

This circumstance was especially elucidated in the discussion of the measurability of electromagnetic field components raised by Landau and Peierls as a serious argument against the consistency of quantum field theory. Indeed, a detailed investigation in collaboration with Rosenfeld showed that all the predictions of the theory in this respect could be fulfilled when due regard was taken to the mutual exclusiveness of the fixation of the values of electric and magnetic intensities and the specification of the photon composition of the field. An analogous situation is met with in positron theory where any arrangement suited for measurements of the charge distribution in space necessarily implies uncontrollable creation of electron pairs.

The typical quantum features of electromagnetic fields do not depend on scale, since the two fundamental constants—the velocity of light c and the quantum of action h—do not allow of any fixation of quantities of dimensions of a length or time interval. Relativistic electron theory, however, involves the charge e and mass m of the electron, and essential characteristics of the phenomena are limited to spatial extensions of the order h/mc. The fact that this length is still large compared with the "electron radius" e^2/mc^2, which limits the unambiguous application of the concepts of classical electromagnetic theory, suggests, however, that there is still a wide scope for the validity of quantum electrodynamics, even though many of its consequences cannot be tested by practical experimental arrangements involving measuring instruments sufficiently large to permit the neglect of the statistical element in their construction and handling. Such difficulties would, of course, also prevent any direct inquiry into the close interactions of the fundamental constituents of matter, whose number has been so largely increased by recent discoveries, and in the exploration of their relationships we must therefore be prepared for a new approach transcending the scope of present quantum theory.

It need hardly be stressed that such problems do not arise in the account of the ordinary physical and chemical properties of matter, based on the Rutherford atomic model, in the analysis of which use is only made of well-defined characteristics of the constituent particles. Here, the complementary description offers indeed the adequate approach to the problem of atomic stability with which we were faced from the very beginning. Thus, the interpretation of spectral regularities and chemical bonds refers to experimental conditions mutually exclusive of those which permit exact control of the position and displacement of the individual electrons in the atomic systems.

In this connection, it is of decisive importance to realize that the fruitful application of structural formulae in chemistry rests solely on the fact that the atomic nuclei are so much heavier than the electrons that, in comparison with molecular dimensions, the indeterminacy in the position of the nuclei can be largely neglected. When we look back on the whole development we recognize indeed that the discovery of the concentration of the mass of the atom within a region so small compared with its extension has been the clue to the understanding of an immense field of experience embracing the crystalline structure of solids as well as the complex molecular systems which carry the genetic characters of living organisms.

As is well known, the methods of quantum theory have also proved decisive for the clarification of many problems regarding the constitution and stability of the atomic nuclei themselves. To some early disclosed aspects of such problems I shall have occasion to refer in continuing the account of my reminiscences of Rutherford, but it would be beyond the scope of this Memorial Lecture to attempt a detailed account of the rapidly increasing insight in the intrinsic nuclear constitution, brought about by the work of the present generation of experimental and theoretical physicists. This development reminds indeed the elders among us of the gradual clarification of the electronic constitution of the atom in the first decades after Rutherford's fundamental discovery.

X

Every physicist is, of course, acquainted with the imposing series of brilliant investigations with which Rutherford to the very end of his life augmented our insight into the properties and constitution of atomic nuclei. I shall therefore here mention only a few of my remembrances from those years, when I often had occasion to follow the work in the Cavendish Laboratory and learned in talks with Rutherford about the trend of his views and the problems occupying him and his collaborators.

With his penetrating intuition, Rutherford was early aware of the strange and novel problems presented by the existence and stability of composite nuclei. Indeed, already in the Manchester time he had pointed out that any approach to these problems demanded the assumption of forces of short range between the nuclear constituents, of a kind essentially different from the electric forces acting between charged particles. With the intention of throwing more light on the specific nuclear forces, Rutherford and Chadwick, in the first years in Cambridge, performed thorough investigations of anomalous scattering of α-rays in close nuclear collisions.

Although much important new evidence was obtained in these investigations, it was more and more felt that, for a broader attack on nuclear problems, the natural α-ray sources were not sufficient and that it was desirable to have available intense beams of high-energy particles produced by artificial acceleration of ions. In spite of Chadwick's urge to start the construction of an appropriate accelerator, Rutherford was during several years reluctant to embark upon such a great and expensive enterprise in his laboratory. This attitude is quite understandable when one considers the wonderful progress which Rutherford hitherto had achieved with the help of very modest experimental equipment. The task of competing with natural, radioactive sources must also have appeared quite formidable at that time. The outlook, however, was changed by the development of quantum theory and its first application to nuclear problems.

Rutherford himself had as early as 1920 in his second Bakerian Lecture clearly pointed out the difficulties of interpreting α-ray emission from nuclei on the basis of the simple mechanical ideas, which had proved so helpful in explaining the scattering of α-particles by nuclei, since the velocity of the ejected particles was not large enough to allow them by reversal to re-enter the nuclei against the electric repulsion. However, the possibilities of penetration of particles through potential barriers was soon recognized as a consequence of wave mechanics, and in 1928 Gamow, working in Göttingen, as well as Condon and Gurney in Princeton, gave on this basis a general explanation of α-decay and even a detailed account of the relationship between the lifetime of the nucleus and the kinetic energy of the emitted α-particles, in conformity with the empirical regularities found by Geiger and Nuttall in the early Manchester days.

When, in the summer of 1928, Gamow joined us in Copenhagen, he was investigating the penetration of charged particles into nuclei by a reverse tunnel effect. He had started this work in Göttingen and discussed it with Houtermans and Atkinson, with the result that the latter were led to suggest that the source of solar energy might be traced to nuclear transmutations induced by impact of protons with the great thermal velocities which, according to Eddington's ideas, were to be expected in the interior of the sun.

During a brief visit to Cambridge in October, 1928, Gamow discussed the experimental prospects arising from his theoretical considerations with Cockcroft, who by more detailed estimates convinced himself of the possibility of obtaining observable effects by bombardment of light nuclei with protons of an energy far smaller than that of α-particles from natural radioactive sources. As the result appeared promising, Rutherford accepted Cockcroft's proposal to build a high-voltage accelerator for such experiments. Work on the construction of the apparatus was started by Cockcroft at the end of 1928 and was continued during the following year with the collaboration of Walton. The first experiments they made with accelerated protons in March, 1930, in which they looked for gamma-rays emitted as a result of the interaction of the protons with the target nuclei, gave no result. The apparatus then had to be rebuilt owing to a change of laboratory and, as is well known, production of high-speed α-particles by proton impact on lithium nuclei was obtained in March, 1932.

These experiments initiated a new stage of most important progress, during which both our knowledge of nuclear reactions and the mastery of accelerator techniques rapidly increased from year to year. Already Cockcroft and Walton's first experiments gave results of great significance in several respects. Not only did they confirm in all details the predictions of quantum theory as regards the dependence of the reaction cross-section on the energy of the protons, but it was also possible to connect the kinetic energy of the emitted α-rays with the masses of the reacting particles which were at that time known with sufficient accuracy thanks to Aston's ingenious development of mass spectroscopy. Indeed, this comparison offered the first experimental test of Einstein's famous relation between energy and mass, to which he had been led many years before by relativity arguments. It need hardly be recalled how fundamental this relation was to prove in the further development of nuclear research.

The story of Chadwick's discovery of the neutron presents similar dramatic features. It is characteristic of the broadness of Rutherford's views that he early anticipated the presence in nuclei of a heavy neutral constituent of a mass closely coinciding with that of the proton. As gradually became clear, this idea would indeed explain Aston's discoveries of isotopes of nearly all elements with atomic masses closely approximated by multiples of the atomic weight of hydrogen. In connection with their studies of many types of α-ray induced nuclear disintegrations, Rutherford and Chadwick made an extensive search for evidence concerning the existence of such a particle. However, the problem came to a climax through the observation by Bothe and the Joliot–Curies of a penetrating radiation resulting from the bombardment of beryllium by α-particles. At first this radiation was assumed to be of γ-ray type, but with Chadwick's thorough familiarity with the multifarious aspects of radiative phenomena he clearly perceived that the experimental evidence was not compatible with this view.

Indeed, from a masterly investigation, in which a number of new features of the phenomenon were revealed, Chadwick was able to prove that one was faced with momentum and energy exchanges through a neutral particle, the mass of which he determined as differing from that of the proton by less than one part in a thousand. On account of the ease with which neutrons, compared with charged particles, can pass through matter without transfer of energy to the electrons and penetrate into atomic nuclei, Chadwick's discovery opened great possibilities of producing new types of nuclear transmutations. Some most interesting cases of such new effects were immediately demonstrated in the Cavendish by Feather, who obtained cloud-chamber pictures showing nitrogen nuclei disintegrating under α-particle release by neutron bombardment. As is well known, continued studies in many laboratories along such lines were rapidly to increase our knowledge of nuclear constitution and transmutation processes.

In the spring of 1932, at one of our yearly conferences in the Copenhagen Institute, where as always we were happy to see many of our former collaborators, one of the main topics of discussion was, of course, the implications of the discovery of the neutron, and a special point raised was the apparently strange circumstance that in Dee's beautiful cloud-chamber pictures no interaction whatever was observed between the neutrons and the electrons bound in the atoms. In relation to this point, it was argued that, owing to the dependence in quantum physics of the scattering cross-section on the reduced mass of the colliding particles, this fact would not be inconsistent even with the assumption of short-range interaction between the neutron and an electron of strength similar to that between the neutron and a proton. A few days later, I got a letter from Rutherford touching incidentally on this point, and which I cannot resist quoting in full:

April 21, 1932.

My dear Bohr,

I was very glad to hear about you all from Fowler when he returned to Cambridge and to know what an excellent meeting of old friends you had. I was interested to hear about your theory of the Neutron. I saw it described very nicely by the scientific correspondent of the Manchester Guardian, Crowther, who is quite intelligent in these matters. I am very pleased to hear that you regard the Neutron with favour. I think the evidence in its support, obtained by Chadwick and others, is now complete in the main essentials. It is still a moot point how much ionization is, or should be, produced to account for the absorption, disregarding the collisions with nuclei.

It never rains but it pours, and I have another interesting development to tell you about of which a short account should appear in Nature next week. You know that we have a High Tension Laboratory where steady D.C. voltages can be readily obtained up to 600,000 volts or more. They have recently been examining the effects of a bombardment of light elements by protons. The protons fall on a surface of the material inclined at 45° to the axis of the tube, and the effects produced were observed at the side by the scintillation method, the zinc sulphide screen being covered with sufficient mica to stop the protons. In the case of lithium brilliant scintillations are observed, beginning at about 125,000 volts and mounting up very rapidly with voltage when many hundreds per minute can be obtained with a protonic current of a few milliamperes. The α-particles apparently had a definite range, practically independent of voltage, of 8 cm in air. The simplest assumption to make is that the lithium 7 captures a proton breaking up with the emission of two ordinary α-particles. On this view the total energy liberated is about 16 million volts and this is of the right order for the changes in mass involved, assuming the Conservation of Energy.

Later special experiments will be made to test the nature of the particles but from the brightness of the scintillations and the trail in a Wilson chamber it seems probable they are α-particles. In experiments in the last few days similar effects have been observed in Boron and Fluorine but the ranges of the particles are smaller although they look like α-particles. It may be, Boron 11 captures a proton and breaks up into three alphas, while fluorine breaks up into oxygen and an alpha. The energy changes are in approximate accord with these conclusions. I am sure you will be much interested in these new results which we hope to extend in the near future.

It is clear that the α-particle, neutron and proton will probably give rise to different types of disintegration and it may be significant that so far results have only been observed in $4n + 3$ elements. It looks as if the addition of the 4th proton leads at once to the formation of an α-particle and the consequent disintegration. I suppose, however, the whole question should be regarded as the result of one process rather than of steps.

I am very pleased that the energy and expense in getting high potentials has been rewarded by definite and interesting results. Actually they ought to have observed the effect a year or so ago but did not try it in the right way.

You can easily appreciate that these results may open up a wide line of research in transmutation generally.

We are all very well at home and I start lectures tomorrow. With best wishes to you and Mrs. Bohr.

Yours ever
RUTHERFORD.

Beryllium shows some queer effects—still to be made definite.
I shall possibly refer to these experiments in the Royal Society discussion on nuclei on Thursday April 25.

Of course, in reading this letter, it must be borne in mind that my previous visits to Cambridge had kept me acquainted with the work in progress in the Cavendish Laboratory, so that Rutherford had no need to specify the individual contributions of his collaborators. The letter is indeed a spontaneous expression of his exuberant joy in the great achievements of those years and his eagerness in pursuing their consequences.

XI

As a true pioneer, Rutherford never relied merely on intuition, however far it carried him, but was always on the look-out for new sources of knowledge which could possibly lead to unexpected progress. Thus, also in Cambridge, Rutherford and his collaborators continued with great vigour and steadily refined apparatus the investigations of the radioactive processes of α- and β-decay. The important work of Rutherford and Ellis on β-ray spectra revealed the possibility of a clear distinction between intranuclear effects and the interaction of the β-particle with the outer electron system and led to the clarification of the mechanism of internal conversion.

Moreover, Ellis' demonstration of the continuous spectral distribution of the electrons directly emitted from the nucleus raised a puzzling question about energy conservation, which was eventually answered by Pauli's bold hypothesis of the simultaneous emission of a neutrino, affording the basis for Fermi's ingenious theory of β-decay.

By the great improvement of accuracy in measurements of α-ray spectra by Rutherford, Wynn-Williams, and others, much new light was thrown on the fine structure of these spectra and their relation to the energy levels of the residual nucleus resulting from the α-decay. A special adventure at an earlier stage was the discovery of the capture of electrons by α-rays which, after the first observation of the phenomenon in 1922 by Henderson, was explored by Rutherford in one of his most masterly researches. As is well known, this work, which brought so much information about the process of electron capture, was to attract new attention a few years after Rutherford's death when, with the discovery of the fission processes of heavy nuclei by neutron impact, the study of the penetration of highly charged nuclear fragments through matter, where electron capture is the dominating feature, came into the foreground.

Great progress both as regards general outlook and experimental technique was initiated in 1933 by the discovery by Frédéric Joliot and Irène Curie of so-called artificial β-radioactivity produced by nuclear transmutations initiated by α-ray bombardment. I need hardly here remind how, by Enrico Fermi's brilliant systematic investigations of neutron induced nuclear transmutations, radioactive isotopes of a great number of elements were discovered and much information gained about nuclear processes initiated by capture of slow neutrons. Especially the continued study of such processes revealed most remarkable resonance effects of a sharpness far surpassing that of the peaks in the cross-section of α-ray induced reactions first observed by Pose, and to Gurney's explanation of which, on the basis of the potential well model, Gamow at once drew Rutherford's attention.

Already Blackett's observations with his ingenious automatic cloud-chamber technique had shown that, in the very process investigated in Rutherford's original experiments on artificial nuclear disintegrations, the incident α-particle remained incorporated in the residual nucleus left after proton escape. It now became clear that all types of nuclear transmutations within a large energy region take place in two well-separated steps. Of these the first is the formation of a relatively long-lived compound nucleus, while the second is the release of its excitation energy as a result of a competition between the various possible modes of disintegration and radiative processes. Such views, in which Rutherford took a vivid interest, were the theme for the last course of lectures which on Rutherford's invitation I gave in 1936 in the Cavendish Laboratory.

Less than two years after Rutherford's death in 1937, a new and dramatic development was initiated by the discovery of the fission processes of the heaviest elements by his old friend and collaborator in Montreal, Otto Hahn, working in Berlin with Fritz Strassmann. Immediately after this discovery, Lise Meitner and Otto Frisch, then working in Stockholm and Copenhagen, and now both in Cambridge, made an important contribution to the understanding of the phenomenon by pointing out that the critical decrease in stability of nuclei of high charge was a simple consequence of the balancing of cohesive forces between the nuclear constituents and the electrostatic repulsion. A closer investigation of the fission process in collaboration with

Wheeler showed that many of its characteristic features could be accounted for in terms of the mechanism of nuclear reactions involving as a first step the formation of a compound nucleus.

In Rutherford's last years he found in Marcus Oliphant a collaborator and friend whose general attitude and working power reminds us so much of his own. At that time new possibilities of research were opened by Urey's discovery of the heavy hydrogen isotope ^{2}H or deuterium, and by the construction of the cyclotron by Lawrence, who in his first investigations on nuclear disintegrations by deuteron beams obtained a number of new striking effects. In the classical experiments of Rutherford and Oliphant, in which by bombardment of separated lithium isotopes with protons and deuterons they were led to the discovery of ^{3}H, or tritium, and ^{3}He, the foundation was indeed created for the vigorous modern attempt to apply thermonuclear reactions to the realization of the full promises of atomic energy sources.

From the very beginning of his radioactive researches, Rutherford was acutely aware of the wide perspectives they opened in several directions. In particular, he early took deep interest in the possibility of arriving at an estimate of the age of the earth and of understanding the thermal equilibrium in the crust of our planet. Even if the liberation of nuclear energy for technological purposes was still to come, it must have been a great satisfaction for Rutherford that the explanation of the hitherto completely unknown source of solar energy as a result of the development he had initiated had come within the horizon in his lifetime.

XII

When we look back on Rutherford's life we perceive it, of course, against the unique background of his epoch-making scientific achievements, but our memories will always remain irradiated by the enchantment of his personality. In earlier Memorial Lectures, several of Rutherford's closest co-workers have recalled the inspiration which emanated from his vigour and enthusiasm and the charm of his impulsive ways. Indeed, in spite of the large and rapidly expanding scope of Rutherford's scientific and administrative activities, the same spirit reigned in the Cavendish as we all had enjoyed so much in the early Manchester days.

A faithful account of Rutherford's eventful life from childhood till his last days has been written by his old friend from the Montreal period, A. S. Eve. Especially the many quotations in Eve's book from Rutherford's astonishingly large correspondence give a vivid impression of his relations with colleagues and pupils all over the world. Eve also does not fail to report some of the humorous stories which constantly grew around Rutherford, and to which I alluded in a speech, reproduced in his book, when Rutherford for the second and last time visited us in Copenhagen in 1932.

Characteristic of Rutherford's whole attitude was the warm interest he took in any one of the many young physicists with whom he came into contact for shorter or longer periods. Thus, I vividly remember the circumstances of my first meeting in Rutherford's office in the Cavendish with the young Robert Oppenheimer, with whom I was later to come into such close friendship. Indeed, before Oppenheimer entered the office, Rutherford, with his keen appreciation of talents, had described the rich gifts of the young man, which in the course of time were to create for him his eminent position in scientific life in the United States.

As is well known, Oppenheimer, shortly after his visit to Cambridge, during his studies in Göttingen was among the first who called attention to the phenomenon of particle penetration through potential barriers, which should prove basic for the ingenious explanation of α-decay by Gamow and others. After his stay in Copenhagen, Gamow came in 1929 to Cambridge, where his steady contributions to the interpretation of nuclear phenomena were highly appreciated by Rutherford, who also greatly enjoyed the bizarre and subtle humour which Gamow unfolded in daily intercourse and to which he later gave so abundant expression in his well-known popular books.

Of the many young physicists from abroad working in the Cavendish Laboratory in those years, one of the most colourful personalities was Kapitza, whose power of imagination and talent as a physical engineer Rutherford greatly admired. The relationship between Rutherford and Kapitza was very characteristic of them both and was, notwithstanding inevitable emotional encounters, marked from first to last by a deep mutual affection. Such sentiments were also behind Rutherford's efforts to support Kapitza's work after his return to Russia in 1934, and were from Kapitza's side most movingly expressed in a letter which I received from him after Rutherford's death.

When, in the beginning of the nineteen thirties, as an extension to the Cavendish, the Mond Laboratory was created on Rutherford's initiative for the promotion of Kapitza's promising projects, Kapitza wanted in its decoration to give expression for his joy in Rutherford's friendship. Still, the carving of a crocodile on the outer wall caused comments which could only be appeased by reference to special Russian folklore about animal life. Above all, however, the relief of Rutherford, in Eric Gill's artistic interpretation, placed in the entrance hall, deeply

F

shocked many of Rutherford's friends. On a visit to Cambridge I confessed that I could not share this indignation, and this remark was so welcomed that Kapitza and Dirac presented me with a replica of the relief; installed above the fireplace in my office at the Copenhagen Institute, it has since given me daily enjoyment.

When, in recognition of his position in science, Rutherford was given a British peerage, he took a keen interest in his new responsibilities as a member of the House of Lords, but there was certainly no change in the directness and simplicity of his behaviour. Thus, I do not remember any more severe utterance of his to me than, when at a Royal Society Club dinner in a conversation with some of his friends I had referred to him in the third person as Lord Rutherford, he furiously turned on me with the words: "Do you lord me?"

In the nearly twenty years during which Rutherford, right up to his death, worked with undiminished energy in Cambridge, my wife and I kept in close touch with him and his family. Almost every year, we were hospitably received in their beautiful home in Newnham Cottage at the backs of the old colleges, with the lovely garden in which Rutherford found relaxation and the upkeep of which gave Mary Rutherford much enjoyable work. I remember many peaceful evening hours in Rutherford's study spent discussing not merely new prospects of physical science but also topics from many other fields of human interest. In such conversations one was never tempted to overrate the interest of one's own contributions, since Rutherford after a long day's work was apt to fall asleep as soon as the discourse seemed pointless to him. One then just had to wait until he woke up and resumed the conversation with his usual vigour as if nothing had happened.

On Sundays Rutherford regularly played golf in the morning with some close friends and dined in the evening in Trinity College, where he met many eminent scholars and enjoyed discussions on the most different subjects. With his insatiable curiosity for all aspects of life, Rutherford had great esteem for his learned colleagues; however, I remember how he once remarked, on our way back from Trinity, that to his mind so-called humanists went a bit too far when expressing pride in their complete ignorance of what happened in between the pressing of a button at their front door and the sounding of a bell in the kitchen.

Some of Rutherford's utterances have led to the misunderstanding that he did not fully appreciate the value of mathematical formalisms for the progress of physical science. On the contrary, as the whole branch of physics, created so largely by himself, rapidly developed, Rutherford often expressed admiration for the new theoretical methods, and even took interest in questions of the philosophical implications of quantum theory. I remember especially how, at my last stay with him a few weeks before his death, he was fascinated by the complementary approach to biological and social problems and how eagerly he discussed the possibility of obtaining experimental evidence on the origin of national traditions and prejudices by such unconventional procedures as the interchange of newborn children between nations.

A few weeks later, at the Centenary Celebrations for Galvani in Bologna, we learned with sorrow and consternation of Rutherford's death, and I went at once to England to attend his funeral. Having been with them both so shortly before and found Rutherford in full vigour and in the same high spirits as always, it was under tragic circumstances, indeed, that I met Mary Rutherford again. We talked about Ernest's great life, in which from their early youth she had been so faithful a companion, and how to me he had almost been as a second father. On one of the following days, Rutherford was buried in Westminster Abbey, close to the sarcophagus of Newton.

Rutherford did not live to see the great technological revolution which was to ensue from his discovery of the atomic nucleus and his subsequent fundamental researches. However, he was always aware of the responsibility connected with any increase in our knowledge and abilities. We are now confronted with a most serious challenge to our whole civilization, to see to it that disastrous use of the formidable powers which have come into the hands of man be prevented, and that the great progress be turned into promoting the welfare of all humanity. Some of us, who were called to take part in the war projects, often thought of Rutherford and modestly strove to act in the way which we imagined he himself would have taken.

The memory which Rutherford has left us remains to everyone who had the good fortune to know and come close to him a rich source of encouragement and fortitude. The generations who in coming years pursue the exploration of the world of atoms will continue to draw inspiration from the work and life of the great pioneer.

The Genesis of Quantum Mechanics[1]

1962

The sixtieth birthday of Werner Heisenberg gives me a welcome opportunity to recount some of my memories from the time when he worked with us in Copenhagen and with such genius created the foundations of quantum mechanics.

I met the young student Heisenberg for the first time almost forty years ago, in the spring of 1922. It was in Göttingen, where I was invited to give a series of lectures on the state of the quantum theory of atomic constitution. In spite of the great progress achieved by Sommerfeld and his school with their supreme mastery of the methods, developed by Hamilton and Jacobi, for treating mechanical systems in terms of invariant action quantities, the problem of incorporating the quantum of action in a consistent generalization of classical physics still contained deep-lying difficulties. The divergent attitudes to this problem gave rise to lively discussions, and I remember with pleasure the interest with which especially the younger listeners responded to my emphasis on the correspondence principle as a guide for the further development.

On this occasion we discussed the possibility that two of Sommerfeld's youngest pupils, of whom he had the greatest expectations, should come to Copenhagen. While Pauli joined our group already in the same year, Heisenberg stayed for another year in Munich at Sommerfeld's advice to complete his doctoral thesis. Before Heisenberg came

[1] Translated from the German article *Die Entstehung der Quantenmechanik*.

to Copenhagen for a longer stay in the fall of 1924, we had the pleasure of seeing him here briefly already the previous spring. The Göttingen discussions were then continued in the Institute as well as on long walks, and I gained an even stronger impression of Heisenberg's rare gifts.

Our conversations touched upon many problems in physics and philosophy, and the requirement of unambiguous definition of the concepts in question was particularly emphasized. The discussions of problems in atomic physics were concerned above all with the strange character of the quantum of action in relation to the concepts employed in the description of all experimental results, and in this connection we also talked about the possibility that mathematical abstractions here, as in relativity theory, might prove to be useful. At that time no such perspectives were yet at hand, but the development of the physical ideas had just entered a new stage.

An attempt to encompass individual atomic reactions within the framework of classical radiation theory had been made in collaboration with Kramers and Slater. Although at first we encountered difficulties regarding the strict conservation of energy and momentum, these investigations led to further development of the notion of virtual oscillators as the connecting link between atoms and radiation fields. Soon after, a great step forward was achieved by the dispersion theory of Kramers, developed on correspondence lines, which established a direct connection with Einstein's general probability rules for processes of absorption and spontaneous and induced emission.

Heisenberg and Kramers immediately took up a close collaboration which resulted in an extension of the dispersion theory. In particular, they investigated a novel type of atomic reaction connected with perturbations caused by radiation fields. However, the treatment remained semi-empirical in the sense that there was still no self-contained basis for the derivation of the spectral terms of atoms or their reaction probabilities. There was then only a vague hope that the connection just mentioned between dispersion and perturbation effects could be exploited for a gradual reformulation of the theory, by which, step by step, every inappropriate use of classical ideas would be eliminated. Impressed with the difficulties of such a programme, we therefore all felt the greatest admiration when the 23-year-old Heisenberg found out how the goal could be reached with one stroke.

With his ingenious representation of kinematical and dynamical quantities through non-commutable symbols the foundation had indeed been laid on which the further development was to rest. The formal completion of the new quantum mechanics was soon achieved in close cooperation with Born and Jordan. In this connection I would like to mention that Heisenberg, on receiving a letter from Jordan, described his feelings in roughly the following words: "Now the learned Göttingen mathematicians talk so much about Hermitian matrices, but I do not even know what a matrix is." Soon afterwards Dirac, whom Heisenberg had told about his new ideas on a visit to Cambridge, gave another brilliant example of a young physicist able to create by himself the mathematical tools suited for his work.

Although decisive progress in the consistent representation of quantum problems had evidently been achieved by the new formalism, it appeared for a time as though the correspondence requirements had not yet all been fulfilled. Thus, I recall how Pauli, whose treatment of the energy states of the hydrogen atom was one of the first fruitful applications of Heisenberg's views, expressed his dissatisfaction with the situation. He stressed that it ought to be obvious that the position of the moon in its orbit around the earth can be determined, whereas, according to matrix mechanics, every state of a two-body system with well-defined energy allows only statistical expectations concerning the kinematical quantities in question.

Just in this respect new light was to come from the analogy between the motion of material particles and the wave propagation of photons, to which de Broglie had referred already in 1924. On this basis Schrödinger succeeded in 1926 by the establishment of his famous wave equation in applying with brilliant success the powerful means of function theory to the treatment of many atomic problems. In regard to the correspondence problem, it was above all essential that every solution of the Schrödinger equation could be represented as a superposition of harmonic eigenfunctions, thus making it possible to follow in detail how the motion of particles can be compared to the propagation of wave packets.

In the beginning, however, a certain lack of clarity remained concerning the mutual relationship between the apparently so different mathematical treatments of the quantum problems. As an example of the discussions from those days, I might mention how a doubt, expressed by Heisenberg regarding the possibility of explaining the Stern–Gerlach effect in terms of wave propagation, was dissipated by Oskar Klein. The latter, who was particularly familiar with the analogy between mechanics and optics, pointed out by Hamilton, and had himself come upon the track of the wave equation, could just refer to Huygens' old explanation of the double refraction in crystals. Schrödinger's visit to Copenhagen in the fall of 1926 afforded a special opportunity for lively exchange of views. On this occasion, Heisenberg and I tried to convince him that his beautiful treatment of dispersion phenomena could not be brought into conformity with Planck's law of black-body radiation without expressly taking into account the individual character of the absorption and emission processes.

The statistical interpretation of Schrödinger's wave mechanics was soon clarified by Born's investigation of collision problems. The complete equivalence of the different methods was also established already in 1926 by the transformation theory of Dirac and Jordan. In this connection I remember how, in an Institute colloquium, Heisenberg pointed out that matrix mechanics permits the determination not only of the expectation value of a physical quantity but also of the expectation values of every power of this quantity, and how in the subsequent discussion Dirac stated that this remark had given him the clue to general transformations.

In the winter of 1925–26 Heisenberg worked in Göttingen, where I also came for a few days. We talked especially about the discovery of the electron spin, whose dramatic history has recently been illuminated from many sides in the Pauli Memorial Volume. It was a great pleasure for the group in Copenhagen that during this visit Heisenberg agreed to take over the lectureship at our Institute after Kramers, who had accepted the chair of theoretical physics in Utrecht. His lectures in the following academic year were appreciated by the students not only for their content but also for Heisenberg's perfect command of the Danish language.

This year was an exceedingly fruitful one for the continuation of Heisenberg's fundamental scientific work. An outstanding achievement was the clarification of the duplicity of the helium spectrum, long considered one of the greatest difficulties in the quantum theory of atomic constitution. Through Heisenberg's treatment of the electron spin in connection with the symmetry properties of the wave functions, the Pauli principle appeared in a much clearer light, and this was at once to bring about most important consequences. Heisenberg himself was led directly to an understanding of ferromagnetism, and soon came the clarification of the homopolar chemical bonds by Heitler and London, as well as Dennison's solution of the old riddle of the specific heat of hydrogen.

In connection with the rapid development of atomic physics in those years the interest was increasingly focused on the question of the logical ordering of the wealth of empirical data. Heisenberg's deep-going investigation of these problems found expression in the famous paper "The Visualizable Content of the Kinematics and Mechanics of Quantum Theory", which appeared towards the end of his stay in

Copenhagen and in which the indeterminacy relations were formulated for the first time. From the beginning, the attitude towards the apparent paradoxes in quantum theory was characterized by the emphasis on the features of wholeness in the elementary processes, connected with the quantum of action. While so far it had been clear that energy content and other invariant quantities could be strictly defined only for isolated systems, Heisenberg's analysis revealed the extent to which the state of an atomic system is influenced during any observation by the unavoidable interaction with the measuring tools.

The emphasis on observational problems again brought to the foreground the questions Heisenberg and I had talked about on his first visit to Copenhagen and gave rise to further discussions about general epistemological problems. Just the requirement that it be possible to communicate experimental findings in an unambiguous manner implies that the experimental arrangement and the results of the observation must be expressed in the common language adapted to our orientation in the environment. Thus, the description of quantum phenomena requires a distinction in principle between the objects under investigation and the measuring apparatus by means of which the experimental conditions are defined. In particular, the contrasts met with here, hitherto so unfamiliar in physics, emphasize the necessity, well known in other domains of experience, to take into consideration the conditions under which the experience has been obtained.

In rendering some of my recollections from the old days, it has above all been on my mind to stress how the close collaboration among a whole generation of physicists from many countries succeeded step by step in creating order in a vast new domain of knowledge. In this period of development of physical science, in which it was a wonderful adventure to participate, Werner Heisenberg occupied an outstanding position.

The Solvay Meetings and the Development of Quantum Physics

1962

The series of conferences originally convened, just fifty years ago, at the far-sighted initiative of Ernest Solvay and continued under the auspices of the International Institute of Physics founded by him, have been unique occasions for physicists to discuss the fundamental problems which were at the centre of interest at the different periods, and have thereby in many ways stimulated modern development of physical science.

The careful recording of the reports and of the subsequent discussions at each of these meetings will in the future be a most valuable source of information for students of the history of science wishing to gain an impression of the grappling with the new problems raised in the beginning of our century. Indeed, the gradual clarification of these problems through the combined effort of a whole generation of physicists was in the following decades not only so largely to augment our insight in the atomic constitution of matter, but even to lead to a new outlook as regards the comprehension of physical experience.

As one of those who in the course of time have attended several of the Solvay conferences and have had personal contact with many of the participants in the earliest of these meetings, I have welcomed the invitation on this occasion to recall some of my reminiscences of the part played by the discussions for the elucidation of the problems confronting us. In approaching this task I shall endeavour to present these discussions against the background of the many-sided development which atomic physics has undergone in the last fifty years.

I

The very theme of the first Solvay conference in 1911, Radiation Theory and Quanta, indicates the background for the discussions in those days. The most important advances in physics in the former century were perhaps the development of Maxwell's electromagnetic theory, which offered so far-reaching an explanation of radiative phenomena, and the statistical interpretation of the thermo-dynamical principles culminating in Boltzmann's recognition of the relation between the entropy and probability of the state of a complex mechanical system. Still, the account of the spectral distribution of cavity radiation in thermal equilibrium with the enclosing walls presented unsuspected difficulties, especially brought out by Rayleigh's masterly analysis.

A turning point in the development was reached by Planck's discovery, in the first year of our century, of the universal quantum of action revealing a feature of wholeness in atomic processes completely foreign to classical physical ideas and even transcending the ancient doctrine of the limited divisibility of matter. On this new background the apparent paradoxes involved in any attempt at a detailed description of the interaction between radiation and matter were early stressed by Einstein, who did not only call attention to the support for Planck's ideas offered by investigations of the specific heat of solids at low temperature but, in connection with his original treatment of the photoelectric effect, also introduced the idea of light quanta or photons as carriers of energy and momentum in elementary radiative processes.

Indeed, the introduction of the photon concept meant a revival of the old dilemma from Newton's and Huygens' days of the corpuscular or undulatory constitution of light, which had seemed resolved in favour of the latter by the establishment of the electromagnetic theory of radiation. The situation was most peculiar, since the very definition of the energy or momentum of the photon, given by the product of Planck's constant and the frequency or wave number of the radiation, directly refers to the characteristics of a wave picture. We were thus confronted with a novel kind of complementary relationship between the applications of different fundamental concepts of classical physics, the study of which in the course of time was to make the limited scope of deterministic description evident and to call for an essentially statistical account of even the most elementary atomic processes.

The discussions at the meeting were initiated by a brilliant exposition by Lorentz of the argumentation based on classical ideas leading to the principle of equipartition of energy between the various degrees of freedom of a physical system, including not only the motion of its constituent material particles but also the normal modes of vibration of the electromagnetic field associated with the electric charge of the particles. This argumentation, following the lines of Rayleigh's analysis of thermal radiative equilibrium, led, however, to the well-known paradoxical result that no temperature equilibrium was possible, since the whole energy of the system would be gradually transferred to electromagnetic vibrations of steadily increasing frequencies.

Apparently the only way to reconcile radiation theory with the principles of ordinary statistical mechanics was the suggestion by Jeans that under the experimental conditions one did not have to do with a true equilibrium but with a quasi-stationary state, in which the production of high-frequency radiation escaped notice. A testimony to the acuteness with which the difficulties in radiation theory were felt was a letter from Lord Rayleigh, read at the conference, in which he admonishes to take Jeans' suggestion into careful consideration. Still, by closer examination it was soon to become evident that Jeans' argument could not be upheld.

In many respects the reports and discussions at the conference were most illuminating. Thus, after reports by Warburg and Rubens of the experimental evidence supporting Planck's law of temperature radiation, Planck himself gave an exposition of the arguments which had led him to the discovery of the quantum of action. In commenting on the difficulties of harmonizing this new feature with the conceptual framework of classical physics, he stressed that the essential point was not the introduction of a new hypothesis of energy quanta, but rather a remoulding of the very concept of action, and expressed the conviction that the principle of least action, which was also upheld in relativity theory, would prove a guidance for the further development of quantum theory.

In the last report at the conference, Einstein summarized many applications of the quantum concept and dealt in particular with the fundamental arguments used in his explanation of the anomalies of specific heats at low temperatures. The discussions of these phenomena had been introduced at the meeting in a report by Nernst on the application of quantum theory to different problems of physics and chemistry, in which he especially considered the properties of matter at very low temperatures. It is of great interest to read how Nernst in his report remarked that the well-known theorem regarding the entropy at absolute zero, of which since 1906 he had made important applications, now appeared as a special case of a more general law derived from the theory of quanta. Still, the phenomenon of the superconductivity of certain metals at extremely low temperatures, on the discovery of which Kamerlingh Onnes reported, presented a great puzzle, which many years later would first find its explanation.

A new feature, commented upon from various sides, was Nernst's idea of quantized rotations of gas molecules, which was eventually to receive such beautiful confirmation in the measurements of the fine structure of infra-red absorption lines. Similar use of quantum theory was suggested in the report by Langevin on his successful theory of the variation of the magnetic properties of matter with temperature, in which he made special reference to the idea of the magneton, introduced by Weiss to explain the remarkable numerical relations between the strength of the elementary magnetic moments of atoms deduced from the analysis of his measurements. Indeed, as Langevin showed, the value of the magneton could at any rate be approximately derived on the assumption that the electrons in atoms were rotating with angular momenta corresponding to a Planck quantum.

Other spirited and heuristic attempts at exploring quantum features in many properties of matter were described by Sommerfeld, who especially discussed the production of X-rays by high speed electrons as well as problems involving the ionization of atoms in the photo-effect and by electronic impact. In commenting upon the latter problem, Sommerfeld called attention to the resemblance of some of his considerations with those exposed in a recent paper by Haas, who in an attempt at applying quantum ideas to the electron binding in an atomic model like that suggested by J. J. Thomson, involving a sphere of uniform positive electrification, had obtained rotational frequencies of the same order of magnitude as the frequencies in optical spectra. As regards his own attitude, Sommerfeld added that instead of trying from such considerations to deduce Planck's constant, he would rather take the existence of the quantum of action as the fundament for any approach to questions of the constitution of atoms and molecules. On the background of the most recent trend of the development this utterance has indeed an almost prophetic character.

Although at the time of the meeting there could, of course, be no question of a comprehensive treatment of the problems raised by Planck's discovery, there was a general understanding that great new prospects had arisen for physical science. Still, notwithstanding the radical revision of the foundation for the unambiguous application of elementary physical concepts, which was here needed, it was an encouragement to all that the firmness of the building ground was just in those years so strikingly illustrated by new triumphs for the classical approach in dealing with the properties of rarefied gases and the use of statistical fluctuations for the counting of atoms. Most appropriately, detailed reports on these advances were in the course of the conference given by Martin Knudsen and Jean Perrin.

A vivid account of the discussions at the first Solvay meeting I got from Rutherford, when I met him in Manchester in 1911, shortly after his return from Brussels. On that occasion, however, Rutherford did not tell me, what I only realized some months ago by looking through the report of the meeting, that no mention was made during the discussions at the conference of a recent event which was to influence the following development so deeply, namely his own discovery of the atomic nucleus. Indeed, by completing in such unsuspected manner the evidence about the structure of the atom, interpretable by simple mechanical concepts, and at the same time revealing the inadequacy of such concepts for any problem related to the stability of atomic systems, Rutherford's discovery should not only serve as a guidance, but also remain a challenge at many later stages of the development of quantum physics.

II

By the time of the next Solvay conference in 1913, the subject of which was the Structure of Matter, most important new information had been obtained by Laue's discovery in 1912 of the diffraction of Röntgen rays in crystals. The discovery removed indeed all doubts about the necessity of ascribing wave-properties to this penetrating radiation, the corpuscular features of which in its interaction with matter, as especially stressed by William Bragg, had been so strikingly illustrated by Wilson's cloud chamber pictures showing the tracks of high speed electrons liberated by the absorption of the radiation in gases. As is well known, Laue's discovery was the direct incentive to the brilliant explorations of crystalline structures by William and Lawrence Bragg, who by analysing the reflection of monochromatic radiation from the various sequences of parallel plane configurations of atoms in crystal lattices were able both to determine the wavelength of the radiation and deduce the type of symmetry of the lattice.

The discussion of these developments, which formed the main topic of the conference, was preceded by a report by J. J. Thomson about the ingenious conceptions regarding the electronic constitution of atoms, by which without departing from classical physical principles he had been able, at least in a qualitative way, to explore many general properties of matter. It is illuminating for the understanding of the general attitude of physicists at that time that the uniqueness of the fundament for such exploration given by Rutherford's discovery of the atomic nucleus was not yet generally appreciated. The only reference to this discovery was made by Rutherford himself, who in the discussion following Thomson's report insisted on the abundance and accuracy of the experimental evidence underlying the nuclear model of the atom.

Actually, a few months before the conference my first paper on the quantum theory of atomic constitution had been published, in which initial steps had been taken to use the Rutherford atomic model for the explanation of specific properties of the elements, depending on the binding of the electrons surrounding the nucleus. As already indicated, this question presented insurmountable difficulties when treated by ordinary ideas of mechanics and electrodynamics, according to which no system of point charges admits of stable static equilibrium, and any motion of the electrons around the nucleus would give rise to a dissipation of energy through electromagnetic radiation accompanied by a rapid contraction of the electron orbits into a neutral system far smaller than the size of atoms derived from general physical and chemical experience. This situation therefore suggested that the treatment of the stability problems be based directly on the individual character of the atomic processes demonstrated by the discovery of the quantum of action.

A starting point was offered by the empirical regularities exhibited by the optical spectra of the elements, which, as first recognized by Rydberg, could be expressed by the combination principle, according to which the frequency of any spectral line was represented with extreme accuracy as the difference between two members of a set of terms characteristic of the element. Leaning directly on Einstein's treatment of the photo-effect, it was in fact possible to interpret the combination law as evidence of elementary processes in which the atom under emission or absorption of monochromatic radiation was transferred from one to another of the so-called stationary states of the atom. This view, which permitted the product of Planck's constant and any of the spectral terms to be identified with the binding energy of the electrons in the corresponding stationary state, also offered a simple explanation of the apparently capricious relationship between emission and absorption lines in series spectra, since in the former we are confronted with transitions from an excited state of the atom to some state of lower energy, while in the latter we generally have to do with a transition process from the ground state with the lowest energy to one of the excited states.

Provisionally picturing such states of the electron system as planetary motions obeying Keplerian laws, it was found possible to deduce the Rydberg constant by suitable comparison with Planck's original expression for the energy states of a harmonic oscillator. The intimate relation with Rutherford's atomic model appeared not least in the simple relationship between the spectrum of the hydrogen atom and that of the helium ion, in which one has to do with systems consisting of an electron bound to a nucleus of minute extension and carrying one and two elementary electric charges, respectively. In this connection it is of interest to recall that at the very time of the conference, Moseley was studying the high-frequency spectra of the elements by the Laue–Bragg method, and had already discovered the remarkably simple laws which not only allowed the identification of the nuclear charge of any element, but even were to give the first direct indication of the shell structure of the electronic configuration in the atom responsible for the peculiar periodicity exhibited in Mendeleev's famous table.

III

Owing to the upsetting of international scientific collaboration by the First World War, the Solvay meetings were not resumed until the spring of 1921. The conference, entitled Atoms and Electrons, was opened by Lorentz with a lucid survey of the principles of classical electron theory, which in particular had offered the explanation of essential features of the Zeeman effect, pointing so directly to electron motions in the atom as the origin of spectra.

As the next speaker, Rutherford gave a detailed account of the numerous phenomena which in the meantime had received such convincing interpretation by his atomic model. Apart from the immediate understanding of essential features of radioactive transformations and of the existence of isotopes which the model provided, the application of quantum theory to the electron binding in the atom had then made considerable progress. Especially the more complete classification of stationary quantum states by the use of invariant action integrals had, in the hands of Sommerfeld and his school, led to an explanation of many details in the structure of spectra and especially of the Stark effect, the discovery of which had so definitely excluded the possibility of tracing the appearance of line spectra to harmonic vibrations of the electrons in the atom.

In the following years it was indeed possible, through the continued study of high-frequency and optical spectra by Siegbahn, Catalan and others, to arrive at a detailed picture of the shell-structure of the electron distribution in the ground state of the atom, which clearly reflected the periodicity features of Mendeleev's table. Such advances implied the clarification of several significant points, such as the Pauli principle of mutual exclusion of equivalent quantum states, and the discovery of the intrinsic electron spin involving a departure from central symmetry in the states of electron binding necessary to account for the anomalous Zeeman effect on the basis of the Rutherford atomic model.

While such developments of theoretical conceptions were still to come, reports were given at the conference of recent experimental progress regarding characteristic features of the interaction between radiation and matter. Thus, Maurice de Broglie discussed some most interesting effects encountered in his experiments with X-rays, which in particular revealed a relationship between absorption and emission processes reminding of that exhibited by spectra in the optical region. Moreover, Millikan reported about the continuation of his systematic investigations on the photo-electric effect, which, as is well known, led to such improvement in the accuracy of the empirical determination of Planck's constant.

A contribution of fundamental importance to the foundation of quantum theory was already during the war given by Einstein, who showed how the Planck formula of radiation could be simply derived by the same assumptions that had proved fruitful for the explanation of spectral regularities, and had found such striking support in the famous investigations by Franck and Hertz on the excitation of atoms by electron bombardment. Indeed, Einstein's ingenious formulation of general probability laws for the occurrence of the spontaneous radiative transitions between stationary states as well as of radiation induced transitions, and not least his analysis of the conservation of energy and momentum in the emission and absorption processes, was to prove basic for future developments.

At the time of the conference, preliminary progress had been made by the utilization of general arguments to ensure the upholding of thermodynamical principles and the asymptotic approach of the description of the classical physical theories in the limit where the action involved is sufficiently large to permit the neglect of the individual quantum. In the first respect, Ehrenfest had introduced the principle of adiabatic invariance of stationary states. The latter demand had come to expression through the formulation of the so-called correspondence principle, which from the beginning had offered guidance for a qualitative exploration of many different atomic pheno-mena, and the aim of which was to let a statistical account of the individual quantum processes appear as a rational generalization of the deterministic description of classical physics.

For the occasion I was invited to give a general survey of these recent developments of quantum theory, but as I was prevented by illness from taking part in the conference, Ehrenfest kindly undertook the task of presenting my paper, to which he added a very clear summary of the essential points of the correspondence argument. Through the acute awareness of deficiencies and warm enthusiasm for any even modest advance, characteristic of Ehrenfest's whole attitude, his exposition faithfully reflects the state of flux of our ideas at that time, as well as the feeling of expectation of approaching decisive progress.

IV

How much remained to be done before appropriate methods could be developed for a more comprehensive description of the properties of matter was illustrated by the discussions at the next Solvay con-ference in 1924, devoted to the problem of metallic conduction. A survey of the procedures by which this problem could be treated on the principles of classical physics was given by Lorentz, who in a series of famous papers had traced the consequences of the assumption that the electrons in metals behaved like a gas obeying the Maxwell velocity distribution law. In spite of the initial success of such considerations, serious doubts about the adequacy of the underlying assumptions had, however, gradually arisen. These difficulties were further stressed during the discussions at the conference, at which reports on the experimental progress were given by experts such as Bridgman, Kamerlingh Onnes, Rosenhain and Hall, and the theoretical aspects of the situation were commented upon especially by Richardson, who also tentatively applied quantum theory on the lines utilized in atomic problems.

Still, at the time of the conference it had become more and more evident that even such limited use of mechanical pictures as was so far retained in the correspondence approach could not be upheld when dealing with more complicated problems. Looking back on those days, it is indeed interesting to recall that various progress, which should be of great importance for the subsequent development, was already initiated. Thus, Arthur Compton had in 1923 discovered the change in frequency of X-rays by scattering from free electrons and had himself, as well as Debye, stressed the support which this

G

discovery gave for Einstein's conception of the photon, notwithstanding the increased difficulties of picturing the correlation between the processes of absorption and emission of photons by the electron in the simple manner used for the interpretation of atomic spectra.

Within a year such problems were, however, brought in a new light by Louis de Broglie's pertinent comparison of particle motion and wave propagation, which was soon to find striking confirmation in the experiments by Davisson and Germer and George Thomson on the diffraction of electrons in crystals. I need not at this place remind in detail how de Broglie's original idea in the hands of Schrödinger should prove basic for the establishment of a general wave equation, which by a novel application of the highly developed methods of mathematical physics was to afford such a powerful tool for the elucidation of multifarious atomic problems.

As everyone knows, another approach to the fundamental problem of quantum physics had been initiated in 1924 by Kramers, who a month before the conference had succeeded in developing a general theory of dispersion of radiation by atomic systems. The treatment of dispersion had from the beginning been an essential part of the classical approach to radiation problems, and it is interesting to recall that Lorentz had himself repeatedly called attention to the lack of such guidance in quantum theory. Leaning on correspondence arguments, Kramers showed, however, how the dispersion effect could be brought in direct connection with the laws formulated by Einstein for the probabilities of spontaneous and induced individual radiative processes.

It was in fact in the dispersion theory, further developed by Kramers and Heisenberg to include new effects originating in the perturbation of the states of atomic systems produced by electromagnetic fields, that Heisenberg should find a stepping stone for the development of a formalism of quantum mechanics, from which all reference to classical pictures beyond the asymptotic correspondence was completely eliminated. Through the work of Born, Heisenberg, and Jordan as well as Dirac this bold and ingenious conception was soon given a general formulation in which the classical kinematic and dynamical variables are replaced by symbolic operators obeying a non-commutative algebra involving Planck's constant.

The relationship between Heisenberg's and Schrödinger's approaches to the problems of quantum theory and the full scope of the interpretation of the formalisms were shortly after most instructively elucidated by Dirac and Jordan with the help of canonical transformations of variables on the lines of Hamilton's original treatment of classical mechanical problems. In particular, such considerations served to clarify the apparent contrast between the superposition principle in wave mechanics and the postulate of the individuality of the elementary quantum processes. Dirac even succeeded in applying such considerations to the problems of electromagnetic fields and, by using as conjugate variables the amplitudes and phases of the constituent harmonic components, developed a quantum theory of radiation, in which Einstein's original photon concept was consistently incorporated. This whole revolutionary development was to form the background for the next conference, which was the first of the Solvay meetings I was able to attend.

V

The conference of 1927, the theme of which was Electrons and Photons, was opened by reports by Lawrence Bragg and Arthur Compton about the rich new experimental evidence regarding scattering of high-frequency radiation by electrons exhibiting widely different features when firmly bound in crystalline structures of heavy substances and when practically free in atoms of light gases. These reports were followed by most instructive expositions by Louis de Broglie, Born and Heisenberg, as well as by Schrödinger, about the great advances as regards the consistent formulation of quantum theory, to which I have already alluded.

A main theme for the discussion was the renunciation of pictorial deterministic description implied in the new methods. A particular point was the question, as to what extent the wave mechanics indicated possibilities of a less radical departure from ordinary physical description than hitherto envisaged in all attempts at solving the paradoxes to which the discovery of the quantum of action had from the beginning given rise. Still, the essentially statistical character of the interpretation of physical experience by wave pictures was not only evident from Born's successful treatment of collision problems, but the symbolic character of the whole conception appeared perhaps most strikingly in the necessity of replacing ordinary three-dimensional space coordination by a representation of the state of a system containing several particles as a wave function in a configuration space with as many coordinates as the total number of degrees of freedom of the system.

In the course of the discussions the last point was in particular stressed in connection with the great progress already achieved as regards the treatment of systems involving particles of the same mass, charge and spin, revealing in the case of such "identical" particles a limitation of the individuality implied in classical corpuscular concepts. Indications of such novel features as regards electrons were already contained in Pauli's formulation of the exclusion principle, and in connection with the particle concept of radiation quanta Bose had at an even earlier stage called attention to a simple possibility of deriving Planck's formula for temperature radiation by the application of a statistics involving a departure from the way followed by Boltzmann in the counting of complexions of a many-particle system, which had proved so adequate for numerous applications of classical statistical mechanics.

Already in 1926 a decisive contribution to the treatment of atoms with more than one electron had been made by Heisenberg's explanation of the peculiar duplicity of the helium spectrum, which through many years had remained one of the main obstacles for the quantum theory of atomic constitution. By exploring the symmetry properties of the wave function in configuration space, considerations independently taken up by Dirac and subsequently pursued by Fermi, Heisenberg succeeded in showing that the stationary states of the helium atom fall into two classes, corresponding to two non-combining sets of spectral terms and represented by symmetrical and antisymmetrical spatial wave functions associated with opposite and parallel electron spins, respectively.

I need hardly recall how this remarkable achievement initiated a true avalanche of further progress, and how within a year Heitler and London's analogous treatment of the electronic constitution of the hydrogen molecule gave the first clue to the understanding of non-polar chemical bonds. Moreover, similar considerations of the proton wave function of the rotating hydrogen molecule led to the assignment of a spin to the proton and thereby to an understanding of the separation between ortho and para states, which, as shown by Dennison, supplied an explanation of the hitherto mysterious anomalies in the specific heat of hydrogen gas at low temperature.

This whole development culminated in the recognition of the existence of two families of particles, now referred to as fermions and bosons. Thus, any state of a system composed of particles with half-integral spin such as electrons or protons is to be represented by a wave function which is antisymmetrical in the sense that it changes its sign, when the coordinates of two particles of the same kind are interchanged. Conversely, only symmetrical wave functions come into consideration for photons, to which according to Dirac's theory of radiation the spin 1 has to be ascribed, and for entities like α-particles without spin.

This situation was soon beautifully illustrated by Mott's explanation of the marked deviations from Rutherford's famous scattering formula, in the case of collisions between identical particles like α-particles and helium nuclei, or protons and hydrogen nuclei. With such applications of the formalism we are indeed not only faced with the inadequacy of orbital pictures, but even with a renunciation of the distinction between the particles involved. Indeed, whenever customary ideas of the individuality of the particles can be upheld by ascertaining their location in separate spatial domains, all application of Fermi–Dirac and Bose–Einstein statistics is irrelevant in the sense that they lead to the same expression for the probability density of the particles.

Only a few months before the conference Heisenberg had made a most significant contribution to the elucidation of the physical content of quantum mechanics by the formulation of the so-called indeterminacy principle, expressing the reciprocal limitation of the fixation of canonically conjugate variables. This limitation appears not only as an immediate consequence of the commutation relations between such variables, but also directly reflects the interaction between the system under observation and the tools of measurement. The full recognition of the last crucial point involves, however, the question of the scope of unambiguous application of classical physical concepts in accounting for atomic phenomena.

To introduce the discussion on such points, I was asked at the conference to give a report on the epistemological problems confronting us in quantum physics, and took the opportunity to enter upon the question of an appropriate terminology and to stress the viewpoint of complementarity. The main argument was that unambiguous communication of physical evidence demands that the experimental arrangement as well as the recording of the observations be expressed in common language, suitably refined by the vocabulary of classical physics. In all actual experimentation this demand is fulfilled by using as measuring instruments bodies like diaphragms, lenses and photographic plates so large and heavy that, notwithstanding the decisive role of the quantum of action for the stability and properties of such bodies, all quantum effects can be disregarded in the account of their position and motion.

While within the scope of classical physics we are dealing with an idealization, according to which all phenomena can be arbitrarily subdivided, and the interaction between the measuring instruments and the object under observation neglected, or at any rate compensated for, it was stressed that such interaction represents in quantum physics an integral part of the phenomena, for which no separate account can be given if the instruments shall serve the purpose of defining the conditions under which the observations are obtained. In this connection it must also be remembered that recording of observations ultimately rests on the production of permanent marks on the measuring instruments, such as the spot produced on a photographic plate by impact of a photon or an electron. That such recording involves essentially irreversible physical and chemical processes does not introduce any special intricacy, but rather stresses the element of irreversibility implied in the very concept of observation. The characteristic new feature in quantum physics is merely the restricted divisibility of the phenomena, which for unambiguous description demands a specification of all significant parts of the experimental arrangement.

Since in one and the same arrangement several different individual effects will in general be observed, the recourse to statistics in quantum physics is therefore in principle unavoidable. Moreover, evidence obtained under different conditions and rejecting comprehension in a single picture must, notwithstanding any apparent contrast, be regarded as complementary in the sense that together they exhaust all well-defined information about the atomic object. From this point of view, the whole purpose of the formalism of quantum theory is to derive expectations for observations obtained under given experimental conditions. In this connection it was emphasized that the elimination of all contradictions is secured by the mathematical consistency of the formalism, and the exhaustive character of the description within its scope indicated by its adaptability to any imaginable experimental arrangement.

In the very lively discussions on such points, which Lorentz with his openness of mind and balanced attitude managed to conduct in fruitful directions, ambiguities of terminology presented great difficulties for agreement regarding the epistemological problems. This situation was humorously expressed by Ehrenfest, who wrote on the blackboard the sentence from the Bible describing the confusion of languages that disturbed the building of the Babel tower.

The exchange of views started at the sessions was eagerly continued within smaller groups during the evenings, and to me the opportunity of longer talks with Einstein and Ehrenfest was a most welcome experience. Reluctance to renounce deterministic description in principle was especially expressed by Einstein, who challenged us with arguments suggesting the possibility of taking the interaction between the atomic objects and the measuring instruments more explicitly into account. Although our answers regarding the futility of this prospect did not convince Einstein, who returned to the problems at the next conference, the discussions were an inspiration further to explore the situation as regards analysis and synthesis in quantum physics and its analogies in other fields of human knowledge, where customary terminology implies attention to the conditions under which experience is gained.

VI

At the meeting of 1930, Langevin presided for the first time, after the demise of Lorentz, and spoke of the loss sustained by the Solvay Institute through the death of Ernest Solvay, by whose initiative and generosity the Institute was created. The President also dwelled on the unique way in which Lorentz had assumed the leading of all previous Solvay meetings and on the vigour with which he had continued his brilliant scientific researches until his last days. The subject of the meeting was the Magnetic Properties of Matter, to the understanding of which Langevin himself had given such important contributions, and the experimental knowledge of which had been so much augmented in those years, especially through the studies of Weiss and his school.

The conference was opened by a report by Sommerfeld on magnetism and spectroscopy, in which he in particular discussed the knowledge of the angular momenta and magnetic moments, which had been derived from the investigations of the electron constitution of atoms, resulting in the explanation of the periodic table. As to the interesting point of the peculiar variation of the magnetic moments within the family of rare earths, van Vleck reported about the latest results and their theoretical interpretation. A report was also given by Fermi on the magnetic moments of atomic nuclei, in which, as first pointed out by Pauli, the origin of the so-called hyperfine structure of spectral lines was to be found.

General surveys of the rapidly increasing experimental evidence about the magnetic properties of matter were given in reports by Cabrera and Weiss, who discussed the equation of state of ferromagnetic materials, comprising the abrupt changes of the properties of such substances at definite temperatures like the Curie point. In spite of earlier attempts at correlating such effects, especially by Weiss' introduction of an interior magnetic field associated with the ferromagnetic state, a clue to the understanding of the phenomena had first recently been found by Heisenberg's original comparison of the alignment of the electron spins in ferromagnetic substances with the quantum statistics governing the symmetry properties of the wave

---

94 ATOMIC PHYSICS AND HUMAN KNOWLEDGE

functions responsible for the chemical bonds in Heitler and London's theory of molecular formation.

At the conference a comprehensive exposition of the theoretical treatment of magnetic phenomena was given in a report by Pauli. With characteristic clearness and emphasis on essentials he also discussed the problems raised by Dirac's ingenious quantum theory of the electron, in which the relativistic wave equation proposed by Klein and Gordon was replaced by a set of first-order equations allowing the harmonious incorporation of the intrinsic spin and magnetic moment of the electron. A special point discussed in this connection was the question of how far one can regard such quantities as measurable in the same sense as the electron mass and charge whose definition rests on the analysis of phenomena which can be entirely accounted for in classical terms. Any consistent use of the concept of spin, just as that of the quantum of action itself, refers, however, to phenomena resisting such analysis, and in particular the spin concept is an abstraction permitting a generalized formulation of the conservation of angular momentum. This situation is borne out by the impossibility, discussed in detail in Pauli's report, of measuring the magnetic moment of a free electron.

The prospects which recent development of experimental technique opened for further investigations of magnetic phenomena were at the meeting reported upon by Cotton and Kapitza. While by Kapitza's bold constructions it had become possible to produce magnetic fields of unsurpassed strength within limited spatial extensions and time intervals, the ingenious design by Cotton of huge permanent magnets permitted to obtain fields of a constancy and extension greater than hitherto available. In a complement to Cotton's report, Madame Curie drew special attention to the use of such magnets for the investigations of radioactive processes, which especially through Rosenblum's work should give important new results as regards the fine structure of α-ray spectra.

While the principal theme of the meeting was the phenomena of magnetism, it is interesting to recall that at that time great advances had also been made in the treatment of other aspects of the properties of matter. Thus, many of the difficulties hampering the understanding of electric conduction in metals, so acutely felt in the discussions at the conference in 1924, had in the meantime been overcome. Already in 1928 Sommerfeld had, by replacing the Maxwell velocity distribution of the electrons by a Fermi distribution, obtained most promising results in the elucidation of this problem. As is well known, Bloch succeeded on this basis by appropriate use of wave mechanics in developing a detailed theory of metallic conduction explaining many features, especially regarding the temperature dependence of the phenomena. Still, the theory failed in accounting for the superconductivity, to the understanding of which a clue has been found only in the last years by the development of refined methods for treating interactions in many-body systems. Such methods also seem suitable to account for the remarkable evidence recently obtained about the quantized character of the supercurrents.

A special reminiscence, however, from the meeting in 1930 is connected with the opportunity it gave to resume the discussion of the epistemological problems debated at the conference in 1927. At the occasion Einstein brought up new arguments, by which he tried to circumvent the indeterminacy principle by utilizing the equivalence of energy and mass derived from relativity theory. Thus, he suggested that it should be possible to determine the energy of a timed pulse of radiation with unlimited accuracy by the weighing of an apparatus containing a clock connected with a shutter releasing the pulse. However, by closer consideration the apparent paradox found its solution in the influence of a gravitational field on the timing of a clock, by which Einstein himself had early predicted the red-shift in the spectral distribution of light emitted by heavy celestial systems. Still the problem, which most instructively emphasized the necessity in quantum physics of the sharp distinction between objects and measuring instruments, remained for several years a matter of lively controversy, especially in philosophical circles.

It was the last meeting which Einstein attended, before the political developments in Germany forced him to emigrate to the United States. Shortly before the following meeting in 1933 we were all shocked by the news of the untimely death of Ehrenfest, of whose inspiring personality Langevin spoke in moving terms when we were again assembled.

VII

The conference of 1933, especially devoted to the Structure and Properties of Atomic Nuclei, took place at a time when this subject was in a stage of most rapid and eventful development. The meeting was opened by a report by Cockcroft, in which, after briefly referring to the rich evidence about nuclear disintegrations by impact of α-particles obtained in the preceding years by Rutherford and his co-workers, he described in detail the important new results obtained by bombardment of nuclei with protons accelerated to great velocities with appropriate high voltage equipment.

As is well known, Cockcroft and Walton's initial experiments on the production of high-speed α-particles by the impact of protons on lithium nuclei gave the first direct verification of Einstein's formula for the general relation between energy and mass which in the following years afforded constant guidance in nuclear research. Moreover, Cockcroft described how closely the measurements of the variations of the cross-section for the process with proton velocity confirmed the predictions of wave mechanics, to which Gamow was led in connection with the theory of spontaneous α-decay developed by himself and others. In the report comprising the whole evidence available at that time as regards so-called artificial nuclear disintegrations, Cockcroft also compared the results of the experiments in Cambridge with proton bombardment with those just obtained in Berkeley with deuterons accelerated in the cyclotron newly constructed by Lawrence.

The following discussion was opened by Rutherford, who, after giving expression for the great pleasure that the recent development of what he used to call modern alchemy had given him, told about some most interesting new results, which he and Oliphant had just obtained by the bombardment of lithium with protons and deuterons. Indeed, these experiments yielded evidence about the existence of hitherto unknown isotopes of hydrogen and helium with atomic mass 3, the properties of which have in recent years attracted so much attention. Also Lawrence, who in more detail described his cyclotron construction, gave an account of the latest investigations of the Berkeley group.

Another progress of the utmost consequence was Chadwick's discovery of the neutron, which represented so dramatic a development, resulting in the confirmation of Rutherford's anticipation of a heavy neutral constituent of atomic nuclei. Chadwick's report, beginning with a description of the purposeful search in Cambridge for anomalies in α-ray scattering, ended up by some most pertinent considerations of the part played by the neutron in nuclear structure, as well as of its important role in inducing nuclear transmutations. Before the theoretical aspects of this development were discussed at the conference, the participants had been told about another decisive progress, namely the discovery of so-called artificial radioactivity, produced by controlled nuclear disintegrations.

An account of this discovery, which was made only a few months before the conference, was included in a report by Frédéric Joliot and Irène Curie, containing a survey of many aspects of their fruitful researches, in which processes of β-ray decay with emission of positive as well as negative electrons were ascertained. In the discussion following this report, Blackett told the story of the discovery of the positron by Anderson and himself in cosmic-ray researches and its interpretation in terms of Dirac's relativistic electron theory. One was indeed here confronted with the beginning of a new stage in the development of quantum physics, concerned with the creation and annihilation of material particles analogous to the processes of emission and absorption of radiation in which photons are formed and disappear.

As is well known, the starting point for Dirac was his recognition that his relativistically invariant formulation of quantum mechanics applied to electrons included, besides the probabilities of transition processes between ordinary physical states, also expectations of transitions from such states to states of negative energy. To avoid such undesired consequences he introduced the ingenious idea of the so-called Dirac sea, in which all states of negative energy are filled up to the full extent reconcilable with the exclusion principle of equivalent stationary states. In this picture the creation of electrons takes place in pairs, of which the one with usual charge is simply lifted out of the sea, while the other with opposite charge is represented by a hole in the sea. This conception was, as is well known, to prepare the idea of antiparticles with opposite charge and reversed magnetic moment relative to the spin axis, proving to be a fundamental property of matter.

At the conference, many features of radioactive processes were discussed, and a most instructive report was given by Gamow on the interpretation of γ-ray spectra, based on his theory of spontaneous and induced α-ray and proton emission and their relation to the fine structure in α-ray spectra. A special point, which was eagerly discussed, was the problem of continuous β-ray spectra. Ellis' investigations of the thermal effects produced by absorption of the emitted electrons especially seemed irreconcilable with detailed energy and momentum balance in the β-decay process. Moreover, evidence on the spins of the nuclei involved in the process seemed contradictory to the conservation of angular momentum. It was, in fact, to evade such difficulties that Pauli introduced the bold idea, which was to prove most fruitful for the later development, that a very penetrating radiation, consisting of particles with vanishing rest mass and spin one-half, the so-called neutrinos, were emitted in β-decay together with the electrons.

The whole question of the structure and stability of atomic nuclei was dealt with in a most weighty report by Heisenberg. From the point of view of the uncertainty principle he had acutely felt the difficulties of assuming the presence of particles as light as electrons within the small spatial extensions of atomic nuclei. He therefore grasped the discovery of the neutron as foundation for the view of considering only neutrons and protons as proper nuclear constituents, and on this basis developed explanations of many properties of nuclei. In particular Heisenberg's conception implied that the phenomenon of β-ray decay be considered as evidence of the creation of positive or negative electrons and neutrinos under release of energy in the accompanying change of a neutron to a proton, or vice versa. In fact, great progress in this direction was soon after the conference achieved by Fermi, who on this basis developed a consistent theory of β-decay, which in subsequent developments should prove a most important guidance.

Rutherford, who with usual vigour took part in many of the discussions, was of course a central figure at the Solvay meeting in 1933, which was to be the last he had the opportunity to attend before his death in 1937 ended a life-work of a richness with few counterparts in the history of physical science.

VIII

The political events leading to the Second World War interrupted for many years the regular succession of the Solvay meetings, which were only resumed in 1948. In those troubled years, the progress of nuclear physics had not relented and had even resulted in the realization of the possibilities of liberation of the immense energy stored in atomic nuclei. Though the serious implications of this development were in everybody's mind, no mention of them was made at the conference, which dealt with the problem of Elementary Particles, a domain in which new prospects had been opened by the discovery of particles with rest mass between that of the electron and the nucleons. As is well known, the existence of such mesons was already, before their detection in cosmic radiation by Anderson in 1937, anticipated by Yukawa as quanta for the short-range force fields between the nucleons, differing so essentially from the electromagnetic fields studied in the first approach to quantum physics.

The richness of these new aspects of the particle problem had just before the conference been revealed by the systematic investigations by Powell and his collaborators in Bristol of the tracks in photographic plates exposed to cosmic radiation, and by the study of the effects of high-energy nucleon collisions first produced in the giant cyclotron in Berkeley. In fact, it had become clear that such collisions lead directly to the creation of so-called π-mesons which subsequently decay under neutrino emission into μ-mesons. In contrast to the π-mesons, the

μ-mesons were found to exhibit no strong coupling to the nucleons and to decay, themselves, into electrons under emission of two neutrinos. At the conference, detailed reports on the new experimental evidence were followed by most interesting comments from many sides on its theoretical interpretation. In spite of promising advances in various directions there was, however, a general understanding that one stood before the beginning of a development where new theoretical viewpoints were needed.

A special point discussed was how to overcome the difficulties connected with the appearance of divergencies in quantum electrodynamics, not least conspicuous in the question of the self-energy of charged particles. Attempts at solving the problem by a reformulation of classical electron theory, fundamental for the correspondence treatment, were clearly frustrated by the dependence of the strength of the singularities on the kind of quantum statistics obeyed by the particle in question. In fact, as first pointed out by Weisskopf, the singularities in quantum electrodynamics were largely reduced in the case of fermions, whereas in the case of bosons the self-energy diverges even more strongly than in classical electrodynamics, within the frame of which, as was already stressed in the discussions at the conference in 1927, all distinction between different quantum statistics is excluded.

Notwithstanding the radical departure from deterministic pictorial description, with which we are here concerned, basic features of customary ideas of causality are upheld in the correspondence approach by referring the competing individual processes to a simple superposition of wave functions defined within a common space–time extension. The possibility of such treatment rests, however, as was stressed during the discussions, on the comparatively weak coupling between the particles and the fields expressed by the smallness of the non-dimensional constant $\alpha = e^2/\hbar c$, which permits a distinction with high degree of approximation between the state of a system of electrons and its radiative reaction with an electromagnetic field. As regards quantum electrodynamics, great progress was just at that time initiated by the work of Schwinger and Tomonaga, leading to the so-called renormalization procedure involving corrections of the same order as α, especially conspicuous in the discovery of the Lamb effect.

The strong coupling between the nucleons and the pion fields prevented, however, adequate application of simple correspondence arguments, and the study of collision processes especially, in which a large number of pions are created, indicated the necessity of a departure from linearity in the fundamental equations and even, as suggested by Heisenberg, the introduction of an elementary length representing the ultimate limit of space–time coordination itself. From the observational point of view such limitations might be closely related to the restrictions imposed on space–time measurements by the atomic constitution of all apparatus. Of course, far from conflicting with the argument of the impossibility in any well-defined description of physical experience of taking the interaction between the atomic objects under investigation and the tools of observation explicitly into account, such a situation would only give this argumentation sufficient scope for the logical comprehension of further regularities.

The realization of prospects involving, as condition of the consistency of the whole approach, the possibility of the fixation of the constant α, as well as the derivation of other non-dimensional relations between the masses of elementary particles and coupling constants, was at the time of the conference hardly yet attempted. Meanwhile, however, a way to progress was sought in the study of symmetry relations, and has since been brought to the fore by the rapid succession of discoveries of a manifold of particles exhibiting a behaviour so unexpected that it was even characterized by various degrees of "strangeness". Thinking of the very latest developments, a great advance has, as is well known, been initiated by the bold suggestion by Lee and Yang in 1957 of the limited scope of the conservation of parity, verified by the beautiful experiments by Mrs Wu and her collaborators. The demonstration of the helicity of the neutrino was indeed anew to raise the old question of a distinction between right and left in the description of natural phenomena. Still, the avoidance of an epistemological paradox in such respect was achieved by the recognition of the relationship between reflection symmetry in space and time and the symmetries between particles and antiparticles.

Of course it is not my intention with such cursory remarks in any way to anticipate problems which will form the main theme for the discussions at the present conference, taking place at a time of new momentous empirical and theoretical advances, about which we are all eager to learn from the participants of the younger generation. Yet we shall often miss the assistance of our deceased colleagues and friends, like Kramers, Pauli, and Schrödinger, who all took part in the conference in 1948, which was the last one I, so far, attended. Likewise we deplore the illness that has prevented the presence of Max Born among us.

In concluding, I want to express the hope that this review of some features of the historical development may have given an indication of the debt which the community of physicists owe to the Solvay Institute, and of the expectations which we all share for its future activity.